The ASQ
Quality Improvement
Pocket Guide

Basic History, Concepts,
Tools, and Relationships

D1593176

The ASQ Quality Improvement Pocket Guide

Basic History, Concepts,
Tools, and Relationships

Grace L. Duffy, editor

ASQ Quality Press
Milwaukee, Wisconsin

American Society for Quality, Quality Press, Milwaukee, WI 53203
© 2013 by ASQ
All rights reserved. Published 2013.
Printed in the United States of America.

22   21   20   19   18   10   9   8   7   6

Library of Congress Cataloging-in-Publication Data

The ASQ quality improvement pocket guide: basic history, concepts, tools, and
relationships / Grace L. Duffy, editor.
     pages cm
Includes bibliographical references and index.

ISBN 978-0-87389-853-9 (pocket guide)

ISBN 978-1-63694-133-2 (paperback)

1. Quality control. 2. Quality assurance. I. Duffy, Grace L., editor. II. American Society for
Quality. III. Title: American Society for Quality quality improvement pocket guide. IV. Title:
Quality improvement pocket guide.
TS156.Q3A74 2013
658.5—dc23   2013003736

ASQ Mission: The American Society for Quality advances individual, organizational, and
community excellence worldwide through learning, quality improvement, and
knowledge exchange.

Attention Bookstores, Wholesalers, Schools, and Corporations: ASQ Quality Press books,
video, audio, and software are available at quantity discounts with bulk purchases for
business, educational, or instructional use. For information, please contact ASQ Quality
Press at 800-248-1946, or write to ASQ Quality Press, P.O. Box 3005, Milwaukee, WI
53201-3005.

To place orders or to request ASQ membership information, call 800-248-1946.
Visit our Web site at www.asq.org/quality-press.

Quality Press
600 N. Plankinton Ave.
Milwaukee, WI 53203-2914
Email: books@asq.org
ASQ   Excellence Through Quality™

Contents

List of
Figures and Tables

Foreword

A quality professional's reference library typically includes classics such as *Quality is Free* and the Juran handbook, the current edition of the ISO 9001 standard, and the most recent publications on topics such as Lean-Six Sigma and social responsibility. These are the references I turn to when I am tasked with answering quality application questions or when I am preparing to deliver a presentation to a diverse audience of quality professionals.

But prior to engaging in any quality-related activity, it's always a good idea to review the basic theory, tools, and methodologies. *The ASQ Quality Improvement Pocket Guide: Basic History, Concepts, Tools, and Relationships* is a single source that will help you accomplish that.

The information contained in this book can be beneficial to any professional needing either an introduction to or a refresh of the basics of quality methods and theories. The explanations are written to address all levels of quality expertise. These quality basics and universal problem-solving tools are the fundamental knowledge you will need to effectively utilize and implement continuous improvement techniques and methodologies.

As chair of the ASQ Quality Management Division, I feel it is an honor to have members with such knowledge and expertise as John Bauer, Grace Duffy, and Russ Westcott, from whose handbook the bulk of the material in this new offering originates. They donate much of their time to advancing the understanding of quality improvement, and this book provides a well-written practical guide to it. I anticipate this will quickly become the most referenced book in my personal library.

– Milton Krivokuca DBA
  ASQ-QMD 2012-2013 Chair

Introduction

This pocket guide is designed to be a quick, on-the-job reference for anyone interested in making their workplace more effective and efficient. It will provide a solid initial overview of what "quality" is and how it could impact you and your organization. Use it to compare how you and your organization are doing things, and to see whether what's described in the guide might be useful.

One of this guide's goals is to pique your interest and convince you why and how this quality stuff works. As a quick start on that goal, take a look at some of the world-class organizations from a broad range of industries that proudly use and promote quality: 3M, Abbott, Alcoa, American Express, Barclays PLC, Baxter International, Boeing, Booz Allen Hamilton, Caterpillar Inc., Cisco, The Coca-Cola Company, Corning, Deere & Company, Dow Chemical, DuPont, FedEx, Ford Motor Company, General Electric, General Motors, Hewlett-Packard, Honeywell International, Intel Corporation, Kraft, Lockheed Martin, Mattel, MEDRAD, Mayo Clinic, Nestlé

Purina PetCare, Northrop Grumman, Raytheon, Research in Motion, Ritz-Carlton Hotel, TATA Group, Xerox.

These organizations and others didn't get to where they are solely via quality practices, but they certainly wouldn't have had even a chance to get there without them. They began their quality journeys with at least some (and probably most!) of the ideas and tools discussed in this guide.

As you make your way through this material, you may recognize things you are *already* somewhat doing but don't refer to as "quality" practices. You should. For others, much of it may feel like basic, common-sense stuff that you could be doing with just a little more effort. You could.

That said, we would be remiss in not emphasizing the even larger effects that quality can have (and has had) when used organization-wide and in much greater depth. You'll see this in the "Quality Models and Systems" section, and you can go into much greater depth via the resources listed there for each model/system.

One of the most important ways to achieve improvement is through the use of effective teams. Every organization already has some teams doing certain projects that they hope will solve a problem or result in improvements, whether they call this "quality" work or not. Although the creation and execution of those teams is obviously an important issue, it is too large in scope for this condensed guide. Thus we have purposely excluded such discussion. If you don't believe your teams are as effective as they could be, refer to the "Additional Reading" section for resources.

The tools of quality described herein are universal. People across the world need to find better, more effective ways to improve the creation and performance of products and services. Since organizational and process improvement is increasingly integrated into all areas of an organization, everyone must understand the basic principles of process control and process improvement. This succinct and concentrated guide can help.

Acknowledgements

We recognize the ASQ Quality Management Division, which created *The Quality Improvement Handbook, Second Edition* from which a great deal of material for this guide was reproduced or adapted. Particular credit is due to the handbook's editors, John E. Bauer, Grace L. Duffy, and Russell T. Westcott.

The editor also expresses gratitude to Paul Daniel O'Mara, CQIA and Managing Editor for ASQ Quality Press, without whom this guide would not have been conceived. Paul had the original vision of an entry-level resource for anyone interested in improving their job and workplace.

Finally, we recognize the manuscript reviewers, Katrina R. Motta, Diane Goiffon, and Ponmurugarajan S. Thiyagarajan, for their conscientious attention to detail and excellent suggestions to make this guide as useful as it can be for our readers.

Part I
History and Concepts

WHAT IS MEANT BY "QUALITY"?

Simply put, when someone says "quality" in a business or management context, they are referring to a specific set of concepts and principles developed over the past century that outline how to accomplish something in a measurable way. This guide aims to give you an overview of those concepts and principles.

The concept of "quality" could be boiled down to mean doing things *well* (create what you intended) and doing things *efficiently* (waste as little time and materials as possible). You accomplish both of these goals by first understanding how well your systems and processes are performing and then by optimizing them. That's a simple way to describe the goal of quality.

The word itself has varying definitions:

- In technical usage:
  - (1) the characteristics of a product or service that bear on its ability to satisfy stated or implied needs
  - (2) a product or service free of deficiencies
- The degree to which a set of inherent characteristics fulfills requirements
- Conformance to requirements
- Fitness for use
- Meeting customer expectations
- Exceeding customer expectations
- Superiority to competitors
- "I'll know it when I see it"

In addition to these various meanings, quality may also be viewed from several dimensions:

- Characteristics such as reliability, maintainability, and availability
- Drivers of quality, such as standards
- Quality of design versus quality of conformance
- Quality planning, control, and improvement

The two quality management system models most frequently used by quality professionals today are the ISO 9000 family of quality management system standards and Lean-Six Sigma. These quality models provide an insight into the components of a quality management system and define quality as it is practiced today. See "Quality Models and Systems" for further information.

Quality is critical for an organization's long-term sustainability, the individuals employed by the organization, and society as a whole. If that sounds unrealistic or naive, visit the ASQ Knowledge Center (http://www.asq.org/knowledge-center) where for free you can read hundreds of case studies proving that these principles work (when done correctly!) and describing how they continue to grow and evolve in their implementation worldwide. This guide also highlights various case studies and/or articles where you can see quality and its tools applied effectively in real-world situations.

HISTORY OF QUALITY

Although the history of quality goes back to ancient times, the modern quality movement had its beginning in the 1920s. It began when Walter Shewhart of Bell Laboratories developed a system known as statistical process control (SPC) for measuring variance in manufacturing production systems. SPC is still used today to monitor consistency and diagnose problems in processes.

Shewhart also created the Plan-Do-Check-Act (PDCA) cycle, which applies a systematic approach to improving work processes. When the PDCA cycle is applied consistently, it results in continuous process improvement. Dr. W. Edwards Deming later referred to this as the Plan-Do-Study-Act improvement cycle.

During World War II, the U.S. War Department hired Deming, a physicist and U.S. Census Bureau researcher, to teach SPC to the defense industry. Quality control and statistical methods were critical factors in the resulting successful war effort. Unfortunately, most of the companies in the United States stopped using these statistical tools after the war.

Meanwhile, the U.S. occupation forces invited Deming to help Japan with its post-war census. He was also invited to present lectures to business leaders on SPC and quality. Japan's acceptance and use of Dr. Deming's techniques had a profoundly positive effect on its economy.

A famous presentation by Deming illustrates his belief that differences in performance most often are caused by the system, not by employees. To demonstrate this point, he put 4,000 beads in a jar, 80% colored white and 20% red. He then chose six participants who, without being able to actually see the beads, "produced" beads for a customer that would not accept red beads by randomly selecting them from the jar. The first person selected a sample of 50 beads. The next person did the same, and so on. When everyone had his or her 50 beads, the number of red beads each participant had was counted. Predictably, each had *some* red beads; each had produced product that the customer would not accept. The experiment showed that it would be a waste of a manager's time to try to find out why one person had 4 red beads and another had 15. Rather, error and variation were found to be within the system itself, not caused by the employees. Deming asserted that management's job should be to improve the system so that everyone could produce as many white beads as possible.

Two other American experts, Dr. Joseph Juran and Armand Feigenbaum, also worked with the Japanese. Both

Deming and Juran drew on Shewhart's work and recognized that system problems could be addressed through three fundamental managerial processes—planning, control, and improvement—and that satisfying the customer's needs was critical. Feigenbaum stressed the need to involve all departments of a company in the pursuit of quality, something he called *total quality control*. The Japanese expanded Juran's customer concept to include internal customers: those people within the organization who depend on the output of other workers.

Kaoru Ishikawa, a Japanese engineer and manager, enlarged Feigenbaum's ideas to include all employees, not just department managers, in the total quality control concept. Ishikawa also helped to create quality circles, which are small teams of managers, supervisors, and workers trained in statistical process control, the PDCA cycle, and group problem solving. Applying these techniques created a flow of new ideas for improvement from everyone in the organization and continuous small improvements that led to better performance. By the 1970s, most large Japanese companies had adopted what Ishikawa called companywide quality control (CWQC) and were producing world-class quality products. The perception of Japanese products changed dramatically as consumers worldwide realized that Japanese cars, electronics, and other exports were extremely innovative, reliable, and in many cases less expensive than comparable products from other countries.

Another quality guru with significant influence was Philip B. Crosby, former corporate vice president for ITT, who defined quality as conformance to requirements. He concluded that it can only be measured by the cost of *non*-conformance, meaning that the only standard of performance is zero defects, which Crosby is primarily known for to this day. In 1979 he wrote *Quality is Free: The Art of Making Quality Certain,* and introduced the concept of *cost of quality* (see "Tools" section).

Crosby believed that all non-conformances are caused, not genetically produced, and that anything that is caused can be prevented. Therefore, organizations should adopt a quality "vaccine" to prevent nonconformance and save money. The three ingredients of the vaccine, according to Crosby, are determination, education, and implementation.

To summarize the contributions of the quality gurus of the 1900s: Dr. Deming emphasized statistical process control, uniformity, and dependability at low cost. "Work smarter, not harder," he said. Juran stressed the human elements of communication, organization, planning, control, and coordination, and said that problems should be scheduled for solution. Crosby introduced the concept of zero defects, and argued that quality is conformance to requirements and that prevention is the best quality management technique.

All of these quality management experts (and many more) agree that quality means meeting customer requirements and that increased productivity is the result of quality improvement. They all advocate management commitment and employee involvement to improve systems and avoid problems, the identification of the most critical problems, the use of statistics and other problem-solving tools, and the focus of all activities on the customer.

It is important to understand that the philosophies of Deming, Juran, Crosby, and the many other quality and management "gurus" are starting points to the development of an organization's quality philosophy. Each organization has unique products, services, cultures, and capabilities. The philosophies of the gurus can help an organization get started, but management, working with all the organization's stakeholders, must develop a philosophy that fits the unique needs of the organization. No one philosophy is totally correct or incorrect. All must be studied and used in the context of how they apply to each individual organization.

CONCEPTS

Systems, Processes, and Variation

As stated at the beginning of this chapter, the concept of "quality" could be boiled down to two ideas: making sure you do things well (create what you intended) and efficiently (waste as little time and materials as possible). You accomplish both of these things by first understanding how well your systems and processes are performing, and then optimizing them.

A *system* can be defined as a set of interrelated or interacting processes. A *process* is a set of interrelated or interacting activities that transform inputs into outputs. A number of processes are required to run a business, such as customer contact, sales, human resources, and product design, development, and delivery. The processes are combined into an interacting network that becomes the total system for meeting the needs of the customer and other stakeholders.

Using a system of interrelated processes to manage an organization is called a *process approach* to management, or simply process management. The process management approach is based on:

- The ability of an organization to identify all its processes and recognize the inputs and outputs of each process

- The documentation of processes so they can be easily implemented

- The identification of the owners of each process

- The implementation of the processes

- The measurement of the outcomes of the implementation

- Continual improvement of the efficiency and effectiveness of the processes

The objectives of an organization are achieved more efficiently when related resources and activities are managed as processes and when the individual processes work together to form an integrated management system.

Process documentation might include these components:

1. A short, simple description of the process and its purpose

2. A description of the process's starting and ending activities

3. A list of inputs required at the process starting points including who provides the inputs, the process supplier

4. A list of outputs at the process ending point including who receives the outputs, the process customer

5. A flowchart of the process; that is, a process map identifying the interfaces of the process with other functions of the organization

6. Identification of the process owner; that is, establishing clear responsibility, authority, and accountability for managing the process

7. The measurements used to identify that the process has been completed successfully

8. A statement of the overall capability of the process

Variations are differences from the designed and expected outputs of a process. Some variation is found in all processes, of course, but the key to controlling processes is to control variation as much as possible.

All variation has some cause. Knowing the causes of variation is important in order to determine the actions that must be taken to reduce the variation. It is most important to distinguish between special cause variation and common cause variation. *Special cause* variation results from unexpected or unusual occurrences that are not inherent in the process. *Common cause* variation results from how the process is designed to operate and is a natural part of the process. Common causes of variation account for approximately 85% of the observed variation in processes. Common causes are sometimes called system causes or chance causes, because the variations they result in are inherent in the system.

Special cause variations can usually be detected and removed by the individuals operating the process first-hand. Common cause variations usually require management action to change some inherent feature of the process. This is sometimes called the "85/15 rule," recognizing that management is responsible for providing the necessary inputs to correct the majority of variation problems, that is, common causes.

Many processes, particularly long-term, high-quantity production processes, lend themselves to the use of statistical process control (SPC). SPC, as discussed in the "History" section, is a method of monitoring a process during its operation in order to control the quality of the products or services while they are being produced rather than relying on inspection of the products or services after completion. SPC involves gathering information (data) on the product or service as it is being created, graphically charting the information on one of several types of control charts, and following the progress of the process to detect unwanted variation.

Knowing *when* variation occurs is the first step in correcting it. That may seem obvious, but some organizations to this day do not have proper measurement systems in place to gather useful data on how their processes are performing. Without that, all you can do is guess at *how* to improve and *whether* you have improved.

The goal of SPC and process management in general is to prevent poor quality in products and services. There are two basic approaches to addressing poor quality. One is to fix what is broken; the other is to design the product or service from the start so that it is what the customer wants and expects the first time it is experienced.

Prevention vs. detection is a quality improvement concept based on the idea that it is far better to prevent errors and mistakes than it is to detect and correct them after they are committed. This also may seem obvious, but many organizations don't operate in this manner. There are various reasons why this is the case, some general and some unique to specific circumstances. One of the more general reasons is that preventing errors is much easier said than done. The rewards ultimately outweigh the effort, but getting started takes a focus and concentrated effort that many organizations can't see the benefits of. Either by choice or by pressure from other sources, they are focused solely on what's easiest in the short term. In many cases, they simply believe it's just as effective to fix problems later. Simply put, the theory and concepts of quality say it isn't, and proponents of quality have been proving it for nearly a century.

The logic of prevention vs. detection is generally acknowledged to be based on the following:

- The avoidance of escalating costs

- The likelihood that errors will be missed in the normal inspection process

In the case of avoiding escalating costs, the further into production or service delivery that an error passes, the more expensive it is to rework or scrap the product or service delivery due to the increasing value-added effort and materials consumed. In fact, much effort has been expended by industrial research and development organizations and by academic researchers to quantify exactly the financial resources consumed, and ultimately wasted, for each step or phase into production or service delivery that bad products or services progress. There are many mathematical models that quantify costs of errors. The most common model is based on a factor of 10, wherein it is assumed that the cost to correct an error increases 10 times for each stage or step in a production or service delivery operation past the point where the original error was made.

Figure 1 illustrates the cost escalation in an example of an incorrect medication prescribed to a patient. The cost of the physician double-checking a prescribed medication before handing the scrip to the patient is minimal. The cost in resources and time becomes larger once the prescription is handed to the pharmacist, who stops normal activities to call the doctor's office, verify the appropriate medication, and subsequently fill the prescription with the correct compound. The most expensive scenario is for the patient (or customer) to find out that the medication was incorrect after he or she has taken it. Not only is the patient out the money for the prescription, but he or she may have experienced adverse effects from the interaction of the wrong prescription with other medications. Remediation of physical damage, plus litigation and loss of reputation, can be tremendously expensive.

The logic of prevention vs. detection should, at this point, be clear. As quality professionals we prefer to prevent errors from happening rather than trying to detect errors that have already occurred. Sampling and inspection simply do not guarantee that all errors will be detected.

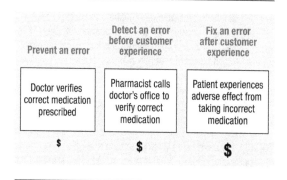

Figure 1 Escalating cost to recover from an error as it passes through production and delivery.

QUALITY MODELS AND SYSTEMS

Systems and processes must be viewed as components of the whole organization. What affects one process or set of processes impacts outcomes of the complete system. In order to effectively manage and control delivery of products and services to customers, we need an overarching model to help us formulate our vision and drive the mission and objectives of the business.

There are several "macro" quality models and systems that help organizations achieve this. The approaches listed hereafter as "macro" are achieved through the use of multiple "micro" quality tools, such as those listed in our "Tools" section.

Keep in mind while reading these explanations of the major approaches to quality and continuous improvement that this guide does not endorse one model over another. Readers are encouraged to look to the needs of their own organization to decide what works best for their operational culture. Also, these approaches are not mutually exclusive; that is, they can be used in conjunction with one another if so desired. Look no further than the various case studies listed in the "Tools" section to see how, in fact, more than one of these is *usually* done at the same time.

At the end of each model/system described, under "MORE," we have listed additional resources that give more in-depth explanations. Consult these for further learning and comprehension.

Baldrige Award

The Baldrige Performance Excellence Program is a national education program based on the Baldrige Criteria for Performance Excellence. The program is a customer-focused change agent that enhances the competitiveness, quality, and productivity of U.S. organizations for the benefit of all citizens. It develops and disseminates evaluation criteria and manages the Malcolm Baldrige National Quality Award in close cooperation with the private sector. It was established by Congress in 1987 and is named after the late Secretary of Commerce Malcolm Baldrige, a proponent of quality management.

Three awards may be given annually in each of six categories:

- Manufacturing
- Service
- Small business
- Education
- Healthcare
- Nonprofit

Organizations that apply for the Baldrige Award are judged by an independent board of examiners, and recipients are selected based on how well they show achievement and improvement in seven areas, known as the Baldrige Criteria for Performance Excellence. The Criteria comprise seven categories:

1. Leadership

2. Strategic planning

3. Customer focus

4. Measurement, Analysis, and Knowledge

5. Workforce focus

6. Operations focus

7. Results

By attempting to satisfy the specific guidelines laid out for each of these Criteria, organizations improve. Many organizations have followed the Criteria without any intention of ever applying for the Award; the improvement resulting from viewing an organization through these requirements is enough reward.

Many state and local governments sponsor quality awards based on the Baldrige Performance Excellence Program Criteria as a means to encourage organizations to advance the level of the quality management processes in their respective communities.

MORE:

- Overview on the ASQ website: http://asq.org/
  learn-about-quality/malcolm-baldrige-award/
  overview/overview.html

- Blazey, Mark L. *Insights to Performance Excellence
  2013-2014: Understanding the Integrated
  Management System and the Baldrige Criteria*
  (Milwaukee: ASQ Quality Press, 2013).

ISO 9001

The term *ISO 9000* is commonly used to refer to a series of
international standards first published in 1987 by the International Organization for Standardization (ISO) in Geneva,
Switzerland. These documents have resulted in profound
changes in the way the quality profession operates. Organizations can use the standards to help determine what is
needed to maintain high levels of quality.

The ISO 9000 family of standards, as they are sometimes
called, represents an international consensus on good management practices. These ensure that an organization has
a system that can deliver a product or services that meet the
customer's requirements. The standards are applicable to any
type of organization, regardless of what the organization does,
how big it is, and whether it's in the private or public sector.

ISO 9001: Quality management systems—Requirements
is the actual requirement standard that outlines the quality
management system elements that must be addressed to
meet customer and applicable regulatory requirements. It is
the only standard in the ISO 9000 family against which third-
party certification can be granted. Since the standard was

first released in 1987, more than one million organizations in 178 countries have achieved ISO 9001 certification. A 2012 analysis of key results from 42 scientific studies showed that implementing the standard enhances financial performance, particularly from increased sales. But the type of implementation matters greatly: organizations aiming at real internal quality improvements gain more than those using ISO 9001 as a "quick fix" in response to quality problems or customer pressure.[1]

Eight quality management principles form the basis of current international quality management requirements, including ISO 9001. These principles are paraphrased as follows:

1. *Customer Orientation.* Organizations must focus on understanding customer needs and requirements. Successful organizations anticipate and exceed customer expectations.

2. *Leadership.* Organizations need strong leaders to establish common goals and direction. Effective leaders establish open environments in which all employees can participate in meeting the organization's goals.

3. *Involvement.* People are the most important part of any organization. Managers must ensure that employees at all levels can fully participate and use their skills to make the organization successful.

4. *Process Management.* The most successful organizations understand that they must manage all their activities as processes.

5. *System Management.* Successful organizations understand that their many individual processes are interrelated and that, in addition to being managed individually, they must be managed within an overall system.

6. *Continual Improvement.* Continual improvement is the key to long-term success and high performance. Successful managers recognize that processes must be reviewed and improved continuously to ensure that the organization stays competitive.

7. *Fact-Based Decisions.* Organizations that base their decisions on factual data are more likely to make the correct decision than those that do not.

8. *Close Supplier Relationships.* Organizations that partner and work closely with suppliers ensure that both the organization and the suppliers are better able to achieve success.

MORE:

- Overview on the ASQ website: http://asq.org/ learn-about-quality/iso-9000/overview/overview.html

- Arter, Dennis R., and J.P. Russell. *ISO Lesson Guide 2008: Pocket Guide to ISO 9001-2008, Third Edition* (Milwaukee: ASQ Quality Press, 2009).

- ASQ. ANSI/ISO/ASQ Q9000-2005 Quality management systems—fundamentals and vocabulary (Milwaukee, WI: ASQ, 2005).

- ASQ. ANSI/ISO/ASQ Q9001-2008 Quality management systems—requirements (Milwaukee, WI: ASQ, 2008).

- Webcast – "ISO 9001:2008 for Small and Medium-Sized Businesses" by Denise Robitaille: http://asq.org/2010/10/iso-9000/iso-9001-2008-for-small-and-medium-sized-businesses.html

PDCA

Dr. W. Edwards Deming was a strong proponent of the plan-do-check-act (PDCA) cycle. The PDCA improvement model is a detailed sequence of steps more associated with the standards or requirements approach seen in the ISO 9000 family of tools. Specific occurrences are identified and detailed targets are set for improvement tasks. Dr. Deming gives credit to his mentor, Walter Shewhart, for the development of the PDCA cycle. PDCA is a four-step model for carrying out change (see Figure 2). Just as a circle has no end, the PDCA cycle (also known as the plan-do-study-act cycle) should be repeated again and again for continuous improvement.

Figure 2   Plan–Do–Check/Study–Act cycle.

PDCA involves the following:

PLAN

- Select project
- Define problem and aim
- Clarify/understand
- Set targets/schedules
- Inform and register the project
- Come up with most suitable recommendation

DO

- Record/observe/collect data
- Examine/prioritize/analyze
- Justify/evaluate cost
- Investigate/determine most likely solutions
- Test and verify/determine cost and benefits
- Test most likely causes

CHECK (STUDY)

- Observe the effects of the change or test
- Consolidate ideas
- Select next project
- Seek approval from management

ACT

- Plan installation/implementation plan
- Install/implement approved project/training
- Maintain/standardize

MORE:

- Webcast – "An Introduction to the PDCA Cycle, Part 1" by Jack ReVelle: http://asq.org/2011/07/continuous-improvement/intro-to-pdca-1.html

Six Sigma

Originally developed by Bill Smith at Motorola in 1986, Six Sigma became well known after Jack Welch made it a central focus of his business strategy at General Electric starting in 1995. Basically, Six Sigma is about collecting data on a process and using that data to analyze and interpret what is happening in that process so that the process can be improved to satisfy the customer.

Sigma is a statistical term that refers to the standard deviation of a process about its mean. In layman's terms, that means how close something comes to being exactly how it was intended to be, whether it's a product or service. Six Sigma means that there will be only 3.4 errors or defects per million opportunities. For example, out of 1 million widgets manufactured, on average only 3.4 will be so far from what they're supposed to be that they are unusable. In a service environment, it could be an average of only 3.4 orders incorrectly inputted or fulfilled for every 1 million received. It should be obvious that this is an extremely low incidence of error in any situation.

Six Sigma is implemented through the Define–Measure–Analyze–Improve–Control (DMAIC) methodology. DMAIC takes a problem that has been identified by the organization and utilizes a set of tools and techniques in a logical fashion to arrive at a sustainable solution. The resultant solution(s) will minimize or eliminate the problem, placing the organization in a more competitive position with its product or service.

MORE:

- Overview on the ASQ website: http://asq.org/learn-about-quality/six-sigma/overview/overview.html

- Mukherjee, Shirshendu. "A Dose of DMAIC" from *Quality Progress* magazine, August 2008.

- Shankar, Rama. *Process Improvement Using Six Sigma: A DMAIC Guide* (Milwaukee: ASQ Quality Press, 2009).

- Webcast – "A Webcast Overview of the Seven Lean Six Sigma Tools" by Jack ReVelle: http://asq.org/2010/08/six-sigma/overview-seven-LSS-tools.html

- Webcast – "The Seven Lean Six Sigma Tools Webcast Series: Value Stream Mapping" by Jack ReVelle: http://asq.org/2010/08/quality-tools/value-stream-mapping.html

- Webcast – "Seven Lean Six Sigma Tools Webcast Series: 5S" by Jack ReVelle: http://asq.org/2010/08/six-sigma/LSS-tools-5s.html

- Webcast – "The Seven Lean Six Sigma Tools Webcast Series: Kaizen" by Jack ReVelle: http://asq. org/2010/08/quality-tools/LSS-tools-kaizen.html

Lean

Lean is a practice that considers wasteful the expenditure of resources for any goal other than the creation of value for the end customer. If you drive improvements by always keeping in mind the end value to the customer, lean proponents say it will improve your products and services as well as your organization as a whole. And these proponents have good reason to say this: lean is derived primarily from the Toyota Production System (TPS), which took Toyota from a small company to the world's largest automaker.

Lean typically divides waste into seven types:

- Overproduction
- Waiting: time in queue
- Transportation
- Non-value-adding processes
- Inventory
- Motion
- Costs of quality: scrap, rework, and inspection

Most recently, many organizations have used Six Sigma and lean at the same time and called it Lean-Six Sigma (LSS) or Lean Sigma. Michael George, in *Lean Six Sigma for Service,*[2] identifies the major areas of emphasis common to the separate disciplines of lean and Six Sigma that have been combined into the LSS methodology:

- System-wide integration
- Leadership involvement and visibility
- Business process focus
- Voice of the Customer driven
- Change management oriented
- Project management dependent

MORE:

- Overview on the ASQ website: http://asq.org/learn-about-quality/lean/overview/overview.html
- Manos, Anthony and Chad Vincent, editors. *The Lean Handbook: A Guide to the Bronze Certification Body of Knowledge* (Milwaukee: ASQ Quality Press, 2012).
- Webcast – "Introduction to Lean in Healthcare and Service": http://asq.org/le/104608/web.html?shl=104608
- Case study – "Lean Six Sigma Increases Efficiency for Financial Services Firm": http://asq.org/2012/04/lean/efficiency-for-financial-services.html

Root Cause Analysis

One of the most valuable tools for identifying variation in performance of processes, products, and services is root cause analysis (RCA). RCA maintains and improves systems and processes through a systematic analysis of observations and data collected about a specific defect in the product or service.

It can take significant time and resources to figure out why something is poorly designed or why something went wrong during development or delivery. It is important to suspend preconceptions and allow those looking into it the freedom to think "outside of the box." They need to get away from what they "know" and explore alternative root causes and contributing factors, unfettered by preconceptions.

Management, for its part, needs to understand that root cause analysis can be as critical a step in the improvement process as anything. Senior management support for the resources to anticipate errors before they occur, or to identify them as they are occurring, is critical in reducing or minimizing the waste of poor quality.

One of the simplest forms of root cause analysis is called *Five Whys*. A full description and examples are given in the "Tools" section. In summary, it consists of asking "Why?" over and over again (often more than five times) until there doesn't appear to be any further answer to it. At that point, the last answer you've come up with may be the root cause.

MORE:

- Overview on the ASQ website: http://asq.org/learn-about-quality/root-cause-analysis/overview/overview.html

- Webcasts – "Root Cause Analysis for Beginners–Part 1 and Part 2" by Jim Rooney: http://asq.org/2011/04/root-cause-analysis-for-beginners-part-1-webcast.html , http://asq.org/2011/04/root-cause-analysis-for-beginners-part-2-webcast.html

- Webcast – "Solution Analysis–Root Cause Analysis" by
  Jack ReVelle: http://asq.org/2011/10/problem-solving/
  solution-analysis-root-cause-analysis-webcast.html

- Andersen, Bjørn, and Tom Fagerhaug. *Root Cause
  Analysis: Simplified Tools and Techniques, Second
  Edition* (Milwaukee: ASQ Quality Press, 2006).

- Okes, Duke. *Root Cause Analysis: The Core of Problem
  Solving and Corrective Action* (Milwaukee: ASQ Quality
  Press, 2009).

Risk Management

By reducing errors or unexpected occurrences in a product or
service, an organization reduces the likelihood that its product
or service will have an adverse effect on its producers,
distributors, customers, and anyone or anything that comes
in contact with it. Therefore, quality is increasingly being seen
as an effective tool for risk management.

The goals of risk management align well with what
the implementation of quality principles can achieve. Per
*ANSI/ASSE Z690.2-2011: Risk Management Principles and
Guidelines,* which is the U.S. adoption of *ISO 31000:2009,* the
management of risk enables an organization to:

- Increase the likelihood of achieving objectives

- Encourage proactive management

- Be aware of the need to identify and treat risk
  throughout the organization

- Improve the identification of opportunities and threats

- Comply with relevant legal and regulatory requirements and international norms

- Improve mandatory and voluntary reporting

- Improve governance

- Improve stakeholder confidence and trust

- Establish a reliable basis for decision making and planning

- Improve controls

- Effectively allocate and use resources for risk treatment

- Improve operational effectiveness and efficiency

- Enhance health and safety performance, as well as environmental protection

- Improve loss prevention and incident management

- Minimize losses

- Improve organizational learning

- Improve organizational resilience

Quality management and actions support all these. In the upcoming years and decades, it is expected that the alignment between risk management and quality will only continue to grow. One of the primary ways is through auditing, a key activity of quality. The "Audit" description in the "Tools" section of this guide gives a description of auditing, but generally speaking it consists of checking that processes and activities are occurring as intended. Specific to risk management, a quality auditor can aid in risk management both by ensuring planned risk management activities are being done and also identifying processes or events that could be significant risks.[3]

MORE:

- Webcast – "The Basics of Risk Management" by the ASQ Government Division: http://asq.org/gov/107563/web.html?shl=107563

- Webcast – "Risks from Suppliers are Ever-Present" by the ASQ Customer-Supplier Division: http://asq.org/cs/103897/web.html?shl=103897

- Case study – Motorola: http://asq.org/six-sigma/2010/02/six-sigma/preempting-problems.pdf

- ANSI/ASSE Z690.1-2011: Vocabulary for Risk Management (U.S. Adoption of ISO Guide 73:2009)

- ANSI/ASSE Z690.2-2011: Risk Management–Principles and Guidelines (U.S. Adoption of IEC/ISO 31000:2009)

- ANSI/ASSE Z690.3-2011: Risk Assessment Techniques (U.S. Adoption of IEC/ISO 31010:2009)

BENEFITS OF QUALITY

By knowing the history of quality in general and some of its concepts and models more specifically, you can already see some of the benefits of it: better products and services, happier customers/users of those products and services, and monetary savings that result from creating those products and services in a smarter way and with less waste.

In this section we'll discuss more specifically how high quality positively impacts all of an organization's stakeholders: employees, the organization itself, customers, suppliers, and the community.

Employees

Well-documented quality systems and processes make the employee's job easier and less frustrating, reduce errors, and allow employees to grow because they are given ready access to information they need to acquire the skills and knowledge to succeed. Organizations should build and maintain work environments that support employees and create a climate conducive to performance excellence and personal and organizational growth. People at all levels are the essence of any organization, and empowering them to fully use their abilities and to be fully involved in the organization's processes benefits the organization. By participating in the development of the organization's processes, employees can see their experience, skills, and ideas being put to use for the benefit of everyone in the organization.

Accurate, complete documentation reduces errors. And with instant access, documentation allows unplanned problems to be dealt with quickly and safely. Well-informed employees have less risk of on-the-job injuries. Employees benefit from the positive culture that exists in a high-quality organization. The reputation, prestige, and image of a high-quality organization make it easier to recruit new employees and play an important part in employee job satisfaction.

Satisfied employees are less likely to want to move on to other organizations.

Quality also benefits the employees involved in producing high-quality products and services by enhancing their feeling of accomplishment in knowing they have done their jobs to the best of their ability. It also strengthens the security of their position by ensuring continued work to meet the demands of satisfied customers. In addition, high-quality products and services sometimes demand higher prices, which can result in higher wages.

The Organization

Quality benefits the organization because it represents the productive and profitable use of the organization's resources. Processes that generate high-quality products and services result in lower costs from repair, rework, and warranty actions. High quality can lead to repeat orders from current customers, and it often enables an organization to win an enhanced reputation and additional orders in the market.

A lack of quality can not only result in lost customers. It can also damage the organization's reputation, which will result in the loss of the future business of those customers. Many say that one dissatisfied customer will tell at least 20 other people how poor your organization's product or service is, and the loss of future orders could be substantial.

The lack of a quality system can create the need for extensive rework, repair, and warranty actions. These actions add extra costs and delays and reduce the productivity of the system. When components are scrapped or services have to be repeated, it is not only time and material cost that are lost but also the cost of all the work done on the product or service (the added value) up to the point at which it is scrapped. Poor quality costs money. Good quality may cost money, too, but the costs of poor quality will always exceed those of good quality.

Good quality can be a powerful marketing tool. Recognition by third-party sources can enhance an organization's ability to market its products and services in ways that competitors can't.

A high-quality organization can focus on continuous improvement—assessing what's happening in the organization and preventing bad product and service quality—rather than just reacting to problems and cases of customer dissatisfaction. This proactive style of management will result in a much more profitable organization than a style that only reacts to problems. It greatly increases the probability of the organization's survival.

Customers

Customer satisfaction can be defined as meeting or exceeding customer requirements for product and service features, price, timeliness, and performance.[4] Quality benefits the customer by increasing customer satisfaction. Fewer defects mean that the customer will be more satisfied. Higher service quality will make the customer's experience more pleasant.

Customers dealing with an organization that has a strong quality program will have fewer complaints because they are being supplied a product or service from better-trained staff following clearer processes and thus making fewer errors. As the organization progressively reduces the time it is forced to devote to correcting mistakes, it can turn to streamlining its processes to make them more cost effective and more customer friendly and to innovating new and better products and processes. Customers will trust the organization more because they know that it takes quality seriously and gives a better level of service.

Quality organizations differentiate themselves from competitors by providing customers with high levels of personalized customer service. Though increased sales and growing profits are generally seen as an accurate measurement of success, customer retention may be the most important measurement of all. High-quality organizations build long-term customer relationships. It will almost always cost more to obtain a new customer than to retain an existing customer.

Suppliers

Quality organizations work closely with their suppliers and share information to ensure that suppliers fully understand the organization's requirements and that the organization knows the capabilities of its suppliers. Suppliers' sales, marketing, and service personnel know what the organization needs and can communicate with the appropriate personnel at their customers' facilities to resolve potential problems before they become serious concerns.

Suppliers benefit from working with quality organizations by developing close partnerships to accomplish mutual goals. Good supplier–organization partnerships tend to have a common set of characteristics, including:

- Reduced cost of inspections
- Less frequent customer audits

- Open sharing of organization and supplier quality information

- Frequent visits to organization and supplier facilities to ensure mutual understanding of each party's relative responsibilities

- Supplier shipments of materials directly to the organization's production line for immediate use

- Decreased expenses from cost sharing

- Reduced risk to the organization because of its ability to use the supplier's knowledge and skills to improve its product or service

The Community and Society

The individual communities in which high-quality organizations operate share in the benefits mentioned above. Think of the many communities and regions that have been devastated by the failure of organizations and industries. The quality, productivity, and competitiveness of high-quality organizations directly affect the viability of the communities they occupy.

Business scandals involving high-profile organizations such as Enron and WorldCom, as well as the U.S. banking system collapse in the mid-2000s, rocked the corporate world and became front-page news. These shook consumer confidence in both business leaders and the economy, creating concern about business ethics and governance. As a result, a concept closely related to quality has become increasingly important: corporate social responsibility (CSR). CSR, which includes such elements as environmental protection, social equity, and economic growth, has a strong affinity with the founding principles of quality management.

ISO's strategic advisory group on CSR describes it as "a balanced approach for organizations to address economic, social and environmental issues in a way that aims to benefit people, communities and society."[5]

CSR includes consideration of such issues as:

- Human rights
- Workplace and employee issues including occupational health and safety
- Unfair business practices
- Organizational governance
- Environmental aspects
- Marketplace and consumer issues
- Community involvement
- Social development

Ethics and values are essentials on which businesses are founded and through which success can be achieved and communities developed. CSR has always been a major influence in the business world and is growing in importance as it is increasingly supported by business models and standards.

Part II
Quality Improvement Tools

H ere are the basic quality improvement tools and how they are used. They are discussed in alphabetical order, not in any order of preference.

We have included only summaries of the concepts of auditing, benchmarking, and cost of quality. Full descriptions of each of these easily fill entire books, thus the information included is purposely succinct; you *will* need to consult additional resources to conduct these quality activities. However, we have provided sufficient information to allow you to apply any of the other tools accurately and effectively.

As we did in the "Quality Models and Systems" section, at the end of each tool description under "MORE" we have listed one or more articles, case studies, or webcasts that provide further depth of explanation. In some cases, examples are included from the Service Quality Body of Knowledge (SQBOK), a project undertaken by ASQ's Service Quality Division "designed to cover the nuances and key attributes of service, relevant quality tools, and how to effectively deliver quality services that satisfy customers." All resources listed

| If you want to: | | | | | | | |
Gather ideas	Group ideas	Analyze	Sequence steps	Draw a picture of data	Track data over time	Prioritize or get group consensus	Show relationships
Affinity diagram	Affinity diagram	Cause-and-effect diagram	Flowchart	Histogram	Check sheet	PICK matrix	Relations diagram
Cause-and-effect diagram	Cause-and-effect diagram	Force-field analysis	Arrow diagram	Pareto chart	Run chart	Multivoting	Scatter diagram
Brainstorming		Relations diagram	Tree diagram	Run chart	Pareto chart	Nominal group technique	
Force-field analysis		Pareto chart		Scatter diagram	Control chart	Relations diagram	
Benchmarking		Five whys		Control chart		Decision matrix	
Audit							

Table 1 Tool selection chart.

Source: Modified from *There Is Another Way: Launch a Baldrige-Based Quality Classroom, Second Edition,* by Margaret A. Byrnes with Jeanne C. Baxter (ASQ Quality Press, 2013).

are "open access" on the ASQ website, meaning you do not need to be a dues-paying member of ASQ to view them.

To give you an idea of what these tools are used for, Table 1 lists some quality improvement activities and which tools align with them. This tool-selection chart is also included in an appendix for quick reference.

AFFINITY DIAGRAM

An affinity diagram helps a team come to consensus about an issue by grouping ideas together.

The team members take turns writing their ideas on separate slips of paper. The team then gathers all the ideas into natural (affinity) groups; in other words, it groups the ideas in a manner that allows those with a natural relationship or relevance to be placed together in the same group or category. Put simply, it starts with specific ideas and helps work toward broad categories for better understanding of an issue.

The steps to generate an affinity diagram are as follows:

1. Identify the problem. Write the problem or issue on a whiteboard or flip chart.

2. Generate ideas. Use an idea-generation technique, such as brainstorming, to identify all facets of the problem. Use index cards or sticky-back notes to record the ideas.

3. Cluster ideas, on cards or paper, into related groups. Ask, "Which other ideas are similar?" and "Is this idea somehow connected to any others?" to help group the ideas together.

4. Create an affinity card (header card) for each group with a short statement describing the entire group of ideas.

5. Attempt to group the initial affinity cards into even broader groups (clusters). Continue until the definition of an affinity cluster becomes too broad to have any meaning.

6. Complete the affinity diagram. Lay out all of the ideas and affinity cards on a single piece of paper or a whiteboard. Draw borders around each of the affinity clusters. The resulting structure will provide valuable insights about the problem.

Figure 3 shows an affinity diagram produced by a team looking for the causes of typographical errors.

MORE:

- Case study – Medrad: http://rube.asq.org/2010/09/six-sigma/critical-elements-major-improvements.pdf

- Case study – Community Consolidated School District 15, Palatine, IL: http://rube.asq.org/2009/08/quality-tools/quality-club-tomorrows-leaders.pdf

- Case study – Hospital example: http://asq.org/healthcare-use/links-resources/affinity-diagram-example.html

- Webcast – "The Seven Management and Planning Tools Webcast Series Overview": http://asq.org/2010/06/quality-tools/the-seven-management-and-planning-tools-webcast-series-overview.html

Causes of Typographical Errors

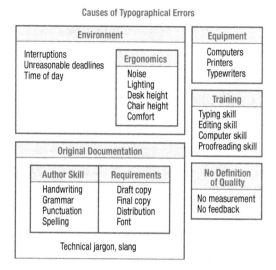

Figure 3 Affinity diagram example.

ARROW DIAGRAM OR
ACTIVITY NETWORK DIAGRAM (AND)

The arrow diagramming method establishes a sequenced plan for accomplishing tasks in a project or process. It may be represented graphically by either a horizontal or vertical structure connecting the planned activities or events.

The arrow diagram can be used to:

- Implement plans for new product or service development and its follow-up

- Develop product or service improvement plans and follow-up activities

- Establish daily plans for experimental trials and follow-up activities

- Establish daily plans for increases in production and their follow-up activities

The arrow diagram illustrates the critical path of a project. This is the flow of critical steps where delays will affect the timing of the entire project and where additional resources can speed up the project.

Figure 4 illustrates a conceptual drawing of the steps for developing a special order product. Although some tasks can be performed in parallel, it takes longer for one sequence of tasks than another. The time for delivering the special order project cannot be any shorter than the longest set of tasks, or the sequence of tasks 1, 2, 4 and 6.

MORE:

- Article – "Beyond the Basics: Seven new quality tools help innovate, communicate and plan": http://asq.org/quality-progress/2012/04/basic-quality/beyond-the-basics.html

Critical Path for Special Product Assembly

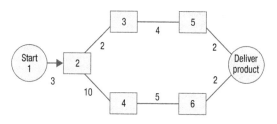

The duration of Task 1, 2, 3, and 5 is 11 days.
The duration of Task 1, 2, 4, and 6 is 20 days.

Figure 4   Arrow diagram example.

AUDITING

At its most basic definition, an *audit* is an assessment to determine whether agreed-upon requirements are being met and will continue to be met. Most people are familiar with the dreaded income tax audit or with financial audits conducted annually by auditors who go through the books of an organization's accounting department. Due to these and other popular examples, many people perceive audits as trying to catch someone doing something wrong.

An audit for quality, a *quality audit,* is like any audit to determine whether agreed-upon requirements are being met. In the pursuit of continuous improvement, a quality audit focuses on identifying ways to improve processes and thus help the organization operate at a higher level than its competitors. An audit can provide management with unbiased facts that can be used to:

- Provide input to management so that they can make informed decisions

- Keep management informed of actual or potential risks

- Identify areas of opportunity for improvement

- Assess personnel training effectiveness and equipment capability

- Provide visible management support of quality, environmental, safety, and other programs

- Ensure ongoing compliance and conformity to regulations and standards

- Determine system and process effectiveness

- Identify system and process efficiencies

Audits are grouped or classified depending on relationships (external and internal), the need for objectivity, and the reason for the audit (verification of product, process, or system). In Figure 5 the circle represents an organization. Outside the circle are the organization's customers and suppliers. All organizations have customer–supplier relationships. Any audits done inside the circle are *internal* audits, and audits done outside the circle are *external* audits.

We further classify first-, second-, or third-party audits based on relationships. *First-party* audits occur within the organization (the same as internal audits or self-assessment) and are inside the circle in Figure 5. *Second-party* audits of suppliers or of customers cross into the circle to audit the organization (their supplier). *Third-party* audits are totally independent of the customer-supplier relationship and are off to the right in the diagram. Third-party audits may result in independent certification of a product, process, or system.

Figure 5   Types of audits.

Source: QualityWBT Center for Education, LLC training materials. Used with permission.

There are three discrete types of audits: product (which includes services), process, and system. A *product audit* is an examination of a particular product or service (hardware, processed material, software), while a *process audit* looks at the processes creating a product or service and whether they are within established limits. It covers only a portion of the total system. A *system audit,* as its name suggests, looks at whether applicable elements of the overall system are appropriate and effective and whether they have been developed, documented, and implemented in accordance and in conjunction with specified requirements.

It is the client's responsibility to determine the purpose of an audit. Then auditors make observations and collect evidence (data). The results of their investigation may be reported as nonconformities/conformities, findings, noncompliances/compliances, defects, concerns, and so on. The audit results can include both positive and negative issues identified.

BENCHMARKING

In benchmarking, an organization compares its own performance for a specific process with the "best practice" performance of a recognized leader in a comparable industry. The evaluation helps the initiating organization identify shortcomings and establishes a baseline or standard against which to measure its progress in improving the process.

The types of approaches to benchmarking include:

- Competitive—comparing with direct competitors locally, nationally, or worldwide

- Functional—focusing on a single function to improve the operation of that particular function

- Performance—analyzing pricing, technical quality, features, and other quality or performance characteristics

- Process—comparing work processes such as billing, order entry, or employee training

- Strategic—studying how companies compete and examining winning strategies that have led to competitive advantage and market success

The basic steps involved in benchmarking are:

1. Identify what is to be benchmarked. Be specific in deciding what the team wants to benchmark.

2. Decide which organizations/functions to benchmark. The comparison should be conducted not only against peers but also against recognized leading organizations with similar functions.

3. Determine the data collection method and collect data. Keep the data collection process simple. There is no one right way to benchmark. It is important to look outward, to be innovative, and to search for new and different ways to improve the process under study.

4. Contact a leader in the benchmark organization. Explain the purpose of the benchmarking study and what information is desired. Give assurance that confidential information will not be asked for. Then inquire about the target organization: ask what they do, why they do it, how they measure and/or evaluate it, what their performance measures are, what has worked well, and what has not been successful.

5. Determine whether what the team has learned from benchmarking can be applied to improve the organization's process. Are there new and different ways to solve the problem or improve the process? Are there other solutions to the problem that the team has overlooked? It's important to keep an open mind about new and perhaps radically different ways of doing things.

MORE:

- Overview on the ASQ website: http://asq.org/learn-about-quality/benchmarking/overview/overview.html

- Case study – Great Ormond St. Hospital: http://rube.asq.org/2008/07/benchmarking/great-ormond-street-hospital-ferrari-formula-one-handovers.pdf

- Case study – RIMS business school: http://rube.asq.org/2011/02/continuous-improvement/business-school-tqm.pdf

- Case study – Texas school district: http://rube.asq.org/2009/10/continuous-improvement/peer-assessments-measure-scorecard-achievement.pdf

- Case study – Genesis Health System: http://rube.asq.org/2010/06/baldrige-national-quality-program/process-improvement-beyond-quality-department.pdf

- Case study – Vancouver Coastal Health: http://rube.asq.org/2012/11/lean/emergency-department-congestion.pdf

- Webcast – "The Seven Management and Planning Tools Webcast Series Overview": http://asq. org/2010/06/quality-tools/the-seven-management-and-planning-tools-webcast-series-overview.html

BRAINSTORMING

Brainstorming is used to generate ideas in a nonjudgmental environment. Group members are presented with the issue and are asked, first, to be wide ranging in their own thinking about the issue and, second, not to criticize the thinking of others. The purpose is to generate a large number of ideas about the issue in a short time period.

As the goal of brainstorming is to generate ideas, make sure everyone in the group understands the importance of postponing judgment until after the brainstorming session is completed.

There are several brainstorming techniques: structured, unstructured, and silent. In most cases, the basic steps involved in brainstorming are as follows:

1. Write the problem or topic on a whiteboard or flip chart where all participants can see it.

2. Write all ideas on the board and do as little editing as possible.

3. Number each idea for future reference.

In *structured* brainstorming (the one-at-a-time or "round-robin" method), one idea is solicited from each person in sequence, participants who don't have an idea at the moment may say "pass," and a complete round of passes ends the session.

The advantage of structured brainstorming is that each person has an equal chance to participate, regardless of rank or personality. The disadvantage of structured brainstorming is that it lacks spontaneity and can sometimes feel rigid and restrictive. Encourage participation and building on the ideas of others.

In *unstructured* (or *free-form*) brainstorming, participants simply contribute ideas as they come to mind. The advantage of free-form brainstorming is that participants can build off each other's ideas. The atmosphere is very informal and may be hectic. The disadvantage of free-form brainstorming is that less assertive or lower-ranking participants may not contribute. An ideal approach is to combine the two methods of structured and unstructured brainstorming. Begin the session with a few rounds of structured brainstorming and finish up with a period of unstructured brainstorming.

In *silent* (or *"write-it-down"*) brainstorming, participants write their ideas on sticky-back notes or small slips of paper that are collected and posted for all to see.

The advantage of silent brainstorming is that it prevents individuals from making disruptive "analysis" comments during the session and provides confidentiality. It can help prevent a group from being unduly influenced by a single participant or common flow of ideas. The disadvantage of silent brainstorming is that the group loses the synergy that comes from an open session. Silent brainstorming is best used in combination with other techniques.

After brainstorming:

- Reduce your list to the most important items
- Combine items that are similar

- Discuss items in turn—each on its own merits

- Eliminate items that may not apply to the original issue or topic

- Give each person one final chance to add items

There are several points to remember about brainstorming:

- Never judge ideas as they are generated. The goal of brainstorming is to generate a lot of ideas in a short time. Analysis of these ideas is a separate process, to be done later.

- Don't quit at the first lull. All brainstorming sessions reach lulls, which are uncomfortable for the participants. Research indicates that most of the best ideas occur during the last part of a session. Try to encourage the group to push through at least two or three lulls.

- Try to write down ideas exactly as they are presented. When you condense an idea to one or two words for ease of recording, you are doing analysis. Analysis should be done later.

- Encourage outrageous ideas. Although these may not be practical, they may start a flow of creative ideas that can be used. This can help break through a lull.

- Try to have a diverse group. Involve process owners, customers, and suppliers to obtain a diverse set of ideas from several perspectives.

MORE:

- Case study – Medrad: http://rube.asq.org/2010/09/ six-sigma/critical-elements-major-improvements.pdf

- Case study – US Navy Ship Maintenance Facility, Japan: http://rube.asq.org/2007/04/teams/simple-process-change-saves-thousands-leads-to-zero-defects.pdf

- Case study – Ford: http://rube.asq.org/2011/12/ six-sigma/ford-team-reduce-costs-environmental-impact.pdf

CAUSE-AND-EFFECT DIAGRAM

The cause-and-effect diagram graphically illustrates the relationship between a given outcome and all the factors that influence the outcome. It is sometimes called an Ishikawa diagram (after its creator, Kaoru Ishikawa) or the fishbone diagram (due to its shape).

The cause-and-effect diagram displays the factors that are thought to affect a particular output or outcome in a system. The factors are often shown as groupings of related sub factors that act in concert to form the overall effect of the group. The diagram helps show the relationship of the parts (and subparts) to the whole by:

- Determining the factors that cause a positive or negative outcome (or effect)

- Focusing on a specific issue without resorting to complaints and irrelevant discussion

- Determining the root causes of a given effect

- Identifying areas where there is a lack of data

Although both individuals and teams can use the cause-and-effect diagram, it is probably most effectively used with a group of people. A typical approach is one in which the team leader draws the fishbone diagram on a whiteboard, states the main problem, and asks for assistance from the group to determine the main causes, which are drawn on the board as the "main bones." The team assists by making suggestions, and eventually the entire cause-and-effect diagram is filled out. Then team discussion takes place to decide which are the most likely root causes of the problem. Figure 6 shows the completed diagram resulting from a team's initial effort to identify potential causes for poor photocopy quality.

The basic steps involved in creating a cause-and-effect diagram are as follows:

1. Draw a long horizontal line with a box at the far right end.

2. Indicate in the box what effect, output, or improvement goal is being portrayed. The effect can be positive (an objective) or negative (a problem). When possible, use a positive effect instead of a negative one. Focusing on problems can produce "finger-pointing," whereas focusing on desired outcomes fosters pride and ownership over productive areas. The resulting positive atmosphere will enhance the group's creativity.

3. Draw four diagonal lines emanating from the horizontal line. Terminate each diagonal line with a box.

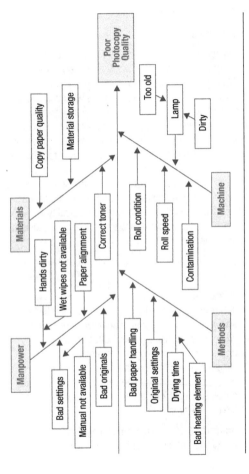

Figure 6 Cause-and-effect diagram example.

4. Label the diagonal lines, often using what are considered to be the four primary categories of potential major causes: Manpower, Machines, Methods, and Materials. Alternatively, use Policies, Procedures, People, and Plant. The team can, of course, substitute other category names if desired.

5. On each of the four diagonal lines, draw smaller horizontal lines ("bones") to represent subcategories and indicate on these lines information that is thought to be related to the cause. Draw as many lines as are needed, making sure that the information is legible. Use an idea-generating technique to identify the factors and sub factors within each major category.

6. Use the diagram as a discussion tool to better understand how to proceed with process improvement efforts and to communicate the many potential causes of quality that impact the effect/output/improvement goal. Look for factors that appear repeatedly and list them. Also list those factors that have a significant effect, based on the data available. Keep in mind that the location of a cause in your diagram is not an indicator of its importance. A sub factor may be the root cause of all of the problems. You may decide to collect more data on a factor that has not been previously identified.

Use this tool when it fits with a particular process improvement effort. It is possible to have a number of cause-and-effect diagrams depicting various aspects of the team's process improvement efforts.

MORE:

- Case study – Community Consolidated School District 15, Palatine, IL: http://rube.asq.org/2009/08/quality-tools/quality-club-tomorrows-leaders.pdf

- Case study – Singapore Housing and Development Board: http://rube.asq.org/2009/06/quality-tools/mojet-pack-product-development.pdf

- Case study – Winston Campus Elementary: http://rube.asq.org/2009/09/continuous-improvement/pdsa-road-map-writing-skills.pdf

- Webcast – "An Introduction to the Seven Basic Quality Tools": http://asq.org/2011/08/quality-tools/an-introduction-to-the-seven-basic-quality-tools-webcast.html

CHECK SHEET

A check sheet is used to record the frequency of specific events during a data collection period. That data can then be converted into readily useful information.

The most straightforward way to use a check sheet is simply to make a list of items that you expect will appear in a process and to make a checkmark beside each item when it does appear. This type of data collection can be used for almost anything, from checking off the occurrence of particular types of defects to counting expected items (for example, the number of times the telephone rings before it is answered). Check sheets can be coupled to histograms to visually depict the information collected.

Figure 7 was used to capture the frequency of reasons for misplaced letters by a post office over a five-day period.

Reasons for Misplaced Letters

Type of Defect	April 23	April 24	April 25	April 26	April 27	Total Defects
Illegible address	‖‖‖ ‖‖‖ ‖‖‖ ‖‖‖ ‖	‖‖‖ ‖	‖‖‖ ‖‖‖ ‖‖‖ ‖‖	‖‖‖ ‖‖‖ ‖‖‖‖	‖‖‖ ‖‖‖ ‖	71
Wrong state	‖‖‖ ‖	‖	‖‖‖	‖‖‖‖	‖‖‖‖	22
Wrong zip code	‖‖‖ ‖‖‖ ‖‖‖ ‖‖‖	‖‖‖‖	‖‖‖ ‖‖‖ ‖‖‖ ‖	‖‖‖ ‖‖‖ ‖	‖‖‖ ‖‖‖ ‖‖‖‖	59
Bad office symbol	‖‖‖	‖‖‖‖	‖	‖‖‖	‖‖‖‖	16
Total Defects	50	19	36	34	29	168

Figure 7   Check sheet example.

A check sheet is a simple way to:

- Collect data with minimal effort
- Convert raw data into useful information
- Translate *perceptions* of what is happening into what is actually happening

The basic steps involved in creating a check sheet are as follows:

1. Clarify the measurement objectives. Ask questions such as "What is the problem?" "Why should data be collected?" "Who will use the information being collected?" and "Who will collect the data?"

2. Create a form for collecting data. Determine the specific things that will be measured and write them down the left side of the check sheet. Determine the time or place being measured and write this across the top of the columns.

3. Label the measure for which data will be collected.

4. Collect the data by recording each occurrence on the check sheet as it happens.

5. Tally the data by totaling the number of occurrences for each category being measured.

6. The data from the check sheet can then be summarized in a number of ways, such as with a Pareto chart or a histogram (see individual entries for both of these for more information).

MORE:

- Article – "Back to Basics: Use Check Sheets To Identify The Causes of Downtime": http://asq.org/quality-progress/2001/04/problem-solving/use-check-sheets-to-identify-the-causes-of-downtime.html

- SQBOK example – http://asq.org/service/body-of-knowledge/tools-check-sheet

CONTROL CHART

A control chart is used to measure sequential or time-related process performance and variability. The control chart is probably the best known, most useful, and most difficult-to-understand quality tool. It is a very sophisticated tool of quality improvement.

In essence, a control chart is a line chart (run chart) with control limits added. The underlying concept is that processes have statistical variation and one must assess this variation to determine whether a process is operating between the expected boundaries or whether something has happened that has caused the process to go "out of control." Control limits are mathematically constructed at three standard deviations above and below the average.

Data are collected by repeated samples and are charted. Based on the graphic presentation of the data on the control chart, one can observe variation and investigate to determine whether it is due to normal, inherent (common) causes or whether it is produced by unique events (special causes).

A typical control chart contains a centerline that represents the average value (mean) of the quality characteristic corresponding to the in-control state. Two other horizontal lines, called the upper control limit (UCL) and the lower control limit (LCL), are drawn. These control limits are identified through equations so that when the process is in control nearly all of the sample points will fall between them. As long as the points plot within the control limits, the process is assumed to be in control, and no action is necessary.

A data point outside of the control limits is interpreted as evidence that the process may be out of control, and investigation and corrective action could be required to find and eliminate the causes responsible for this behavior. The control points are connected with straight lines for easy visualization. Even if all the points plot inside the control limits, if over several consecutive time intervals they behave in a repetitive or other nonrandom manner, then this is an indication that the process is out of control. Figure 8 shows points representing the variable measurement taken for each of 10 items.

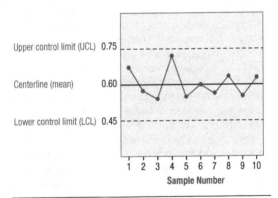

Figure 8 Control chart example (process in control).

Note that upper and lower control limits are not specification limits. They have a mathematical relationship to the process outputs. Specification limits are based on product or customer requirements.

There are several types of control charts, but all have the same basic structure. The two main categories of control charts are those that display attribute data and those that display variables data:

- *Attribute data.* This category of control chart displays data that result from counting the number of occurrences or items in a single category of similar items or occurrences. These "count" data may be expressed as pass/fail, yes/no, or presence/absence of a defect. Charting the proportion of failed items results in the ability to observe whether failures are in control or out of control.

- *Variables data.* This category of control chart displays values resulting from the measurement of a continuous variable. Examples of variables data are elapsed time, temperature, and radiation dose. Explanation of these chart types and their characteristics requires more space than is available in this publication.

Control charts may be used to:

- Display and understand variation in a process

- Help the investigator determine when actual events "fall outside of process limits of tolerance (control limits) and become "outliers" that are out of control

- Determine whether quality improvement efforts have made a statistically significant difference to a key quality indicator

- Monitor a process output (such as cost or a quality characteristic) to determine whether special causes of variation have occurred in the process

- Determine how capable the current process is of meeting specifications, if specification limits exist, and of allowing for improvements in the process

The benefits of control charts are that they:

- Help organizations recognize and understand variation and how to control it

- Help identify special causes of variation and changes in performance

- Keep organizations from trying to fix a process that is varying randomly within control limits (that is, no special causes are present)

- Assist in the diagnosis of process problems

- Determine whether process improvements are having the desired effects

A control chart indicates an out-of-control condition when data points fall beyond the control limits or when the plotted points exhibit some non-random pattern of behavior. Figure 9 illustrates a process where two points are outside the upper or lower control limits. It also contains a run of more than six points in a row steadily decreasing. Both are indicators of an out of control process.

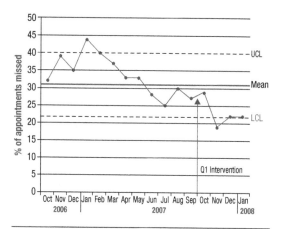

Figure 9   Control chart example (out of control process).

MORE:

- Case study – Akron Children's Hospital: http://rube.
  asq.org/2011/04/six-sigma/reducing-wait-for-mri-
  exams-gives-akron-childrens-hospital-competitive-
  edge.pdf

- Article – "Challenges With Churn": http://rube.asq.org/
  six-sigma/2011/11/customer-satisfaction-and-value/
  challenges-with-churn.pdf

- Article – "Statistical Engineering to Stabilize
  Vaccine Supply": http://rube.asq.org/quality-
  engineering/2012/04/statistics/stabilize-vaccine-
  supply.pdf

- Article – "A Dose of DMAIC": http://asq.org/quality-progress/2008/08/six-sigma/a-dose-of-dmaic.html

- Webcast – "The Seven Basic Quality Tools Webcast: Control Charts": http://asq.org/2010/06/basic-quality/control-charts.html

- Webcast – "An Introduction to the Seven Basic Quality Tools": http://asq.org/2011/08/quality-tools/an-introduction-to-the-seven-basic-quality-tools-webcast.html

COST OF QUALITY

Cost of quality is a methodology that allows an organization to determine the extent to which its resources are used for activities that prevent poor quality, that appraise the quality of the organization's products or services, and that result from internal and external failures. Having such information allows an organization to determine the potential savings to be gained by implementing process improvements.

Quality-related activities that incur costs may be divided into prevention costs, appraisal costs, and internal and external failure costs.

Prevention costs are incurred to prevent or avoid quality problems. These costs are associated with the design, implementation, and maintenance of the quality management system. They are planned and incurred before actual operation, and they could include:

- Product or service requirements—establishment of specifications for incoming materials, processes, finished products, and services

- Quality planning—creation of plans for quality, reliability, operations, production, and inspection

- Quality assurance—creation and maintenance of the quality system

- Training—development, preparation, and maintenance of programs

Appraisal costs are associated with measuring and monitoring activities related to quality. These costs are associated with the suppliers' and customers' evaluation of purchased materials, processes, products, and services to ensure that they conform to specifications. They could include:

- Verification—checking of incoming material, process setup, and products against agreed specifications

- Quality audits—confirmation that the quality system is functioning correctly

- Supplier rating—assessment and approval of suppliers of products and services

Internal failure costs are incurred to remedy defects discovered before the product or service is delivered to the customer. These costs occur when the results of work fail to reach design quality standards and are detected before they are transferred to the customer. They could include:

- Waste—performance of unnecessary work or holding of stock as a result of errors, poor organization, or communication

- Scrap—defective product or material that cannot be repaired, used, or sold

- Rework or rectification—**correction of defective material or errors**

- Failure analysis—**activity required to establish the causes of internal product or service failure**

External failure costs are incurred to remedy defects discovered by customers. These costs occur when products or services that fail to reach design quality standards are not detected until after transfer to the customer. They could include:

- Repairs and servicing—**of both returned products and those in the field**

- Warranty claims—**failed products that are replaced or services that are re-performed under a guarantee**

- Complaints—**all work and costs associated with handling and servicing customers' complaints**

- Returns—**handling and investigation of rejected or recalled products, including transport costs**

The costs of doing a quality job, conducting quality improvements, and achieving goals must be carefully managed so that the long-term effect of quality on the organization is a desirable one. These costs must be a true measure of the quality effort, and they are best determined from an analysis of the costs of quality. Such an analysis provides a method of assessing the effectiveness of the management of quality and a means of determining problem areas, opportunities, savings, and action priorities.

Cost of quality is also an important communication tool. Crosby demonstrated what a powerful tool it could be to raise awareness of the importance of quality. He referred to the measure as the "price of nonconformance" and argued that organizations choose to pay for poor quality. Many organizations will have true quality-related costs as high as 15% to 20% of sales revenue, some going as high as 40% of total operations. A general rule of thumb is that costs of poor quality in a thriving company will be about 10% to 15% of operations. Effective quality improvement programs can reduce this substantially, thus making a direct contribution to profits.

The quality cost system, once established, should become dynamic and have a positive impact on the achievement of the organization's mission, goals, and objectives.

MORE:

- Overview on the ASQ website: http://asq.org/learn-about-quality/cost-of-quality/overview/overview.html

- Case study – CRC: http://rube.asq.org/2006/04/cost-of-quality/using-cost-of-quality-to-improve-business-results.pdf

DECISION MATRIX

You may have seen or used one of these, as this tool goes by many other names: a Pugh matrix, decision grid, selection matrix or grid, problem matrix, problem selection matrix, opportunity analysis, solution matrix, criteria rating form, or criteria-based matrix.

However referred to, what we'll call a decision matrix is used to evaluate and prioritize a list of options. A team establishes a list of weighted criteria and then evaluates each option against those criteria.

The steps in creating a decision matrix are:

1. Brainstorm the evaluation criteria appropriate to the situation. If possible, involve customers in this process.

2. Discuss and refine the list of criteria. Identify any criteria that must be included and any that must not be included. Reduce the list of criteria to those that the team believes are most important. Tools such as list reduction and multivoting may be useful here.

3. Assign a relative weight to each criterion based on how important that criterion is to the situation. Do this by distributing 10 points among the criteria. The assignment can be done by discussion and consensus. Or ask each member to assign weights and then sum the numbers for each criterion to arrive at a composite team weighting.

4. Draw an L-shaped matrix. Write the criteria and their weights as labels along one edge and the list of options along the other edge. Usually, whichever group has fewer items occupies the vertical edge.

5. Evaluate each choice against the criteria. There are three ways to do this:

   Method 1: Establish a rating scale for each criterion. Some options are:

   • 1, 2, 3 (1 = slight extent, 2 = some extent, 3 = great extent)

- 1, 2, 3 (1 = low, 2 = medium, 3 = high)
- 1, 2, 3, 4, 5 (1 = little to 5 = great)
- 1, 4, 9 (1 = low, 4 = moderate, 9 = high)

Make sure that your rating scales are consistent. Word your criteria and set the scales so that the high end of the scale (9, 5 or 3) is always the rating that would tend to make you select that option: most impact on customers, greatest importance, least difficulty, greatest likelihood of success. For example:

Importance	Cost	Difficulty
low = 1, high = 5	high = 1, low = 5	high = 1, low = 5

Method 2: For each criterion, rank-order all options according to how well each meets the criterion. Number them with 1 being the option that is least desirable according to that criterion.

Method 3, Pugh matrix: Establish a baseline, which may be one of the alternatives or the current product or service. For each criterion, rate each other alternative in comparison to the baseline, using scores of worse (−1), same (0), or better (+1). Finer rating scales can be used, such as 2, 1, 0, −1, −2 for a five-point scale or 3, 2, 1, 0, −1, −2, −3 for a seven-point scale. Again, be sure that positive numbers reflect desirable ratings.

6. Multiply each option's rating by the weight. Add the points for each option. The option with the highest score will not necessarily be the one to choose, but the relative scores can generate meaningful discussion and lead the team toward consensus.

Figure 10 shows a decision matrix example from the customer service team at the fictitious Parisian Experience restaurant. It was trying to decide which aspect of the overall problem of "long wait time" to tackle first. The problems identified are customers waiting for the host, the waiter, the food, and the check.

The criteria they identified are "Customer pain" (how much does this negatively affect the customer?), "Ease to solve," "Effect on other systems," and "Speed to solve." Originally, the criteria "Ease to solve" was written as "Difficulty to solve," but that wording reversed the rating scale. With the current wording, a high rating on each criterion defines a state that would encourage selecting the problem: high customer pain, very easy to solve, high effect on other systems, and quick solution.

"Customer pain" has been weighted with 5 points, showing that the team considers it by far the most important criterion, compared to 1 or 2 points for the others.

Each rating is multiplied by the weight for that criterion. For example, "Customer pain" (weight of 5) for "Customers wait for host" rates high (3) for a score of 15. The scores are added across the rows to obtain a total for each problem. "Customers wait for host" has the highest score at 28. Since the next highest score is 18, the host problem probably should be addressed first.

Decision Matrix: Long Wait Time

Criteria → ↓ Problems	Customer pain 5	Ease to solve 2	Effect on other systems 1	Speed to solve 2	
Customers wait for host	High—Nothing else for customer to do 3 × 5 = 15	Medium— Involves host and bussers 2 × 2 = 4	High—Gets customer off to bad start 3 × 1 = 3	High—Observations show adequate empty tables 3 × 2 = 6	28
Customers wait for waiter	Medium—Customer can eat breadsticks 2 × 5 = 10	Medium— Involves host and waiters 2 × 2 = 4	Medium—Customer still feels unattended 2 × 1 = 2	Low—Waiters involved in many activities 1 × 2 = 2	18
Customers wait for food	Medium—Ambiance is nice 2 × 5 = 10	Low—Involves waiters and kitchen 1 × 2 = 2	Medium—Might result in extra trips to kitchen for waiter 2 × 1 = 2	Low—Kitchen design/space limited 1 × 2 = 2	16
Customers wait for check	Low—Customers can relax over coffee, mints 1 × 5 = 5	Medium— Involves waiters and host 2 × 2 = 4	Medium—Customers waiting for tables might notice 2 × 1 = 2	Low— Computerized ticket system is needed 1 × 2 = 2	13

Figure 10 Decision matrix example.

FIVE WHYS

The Five Whys technique is a simple way to get at the root causes of a problem by asking "why?" after each successive response. Asking why is a favorite technique of the Japanese for discovering the root cause (or causes) of a problem. By asking the question "why?" a number of times (five is only an arbitrary figure), you peel away layer after layer of "symptoms" to get to the real heart of an issue. You may never know ahead of time exactly how many times you'll have to ask why. Figure 11 is an example of the Five Whys technique applied to the issue of childhood obesity.

The basic steps involved in using Five Whys are:

1. Describe the problem in very specific terms.

2. Ask why it happens.

3. If the answer doesn't identify a root cause, ask why again. You know you've identified the root cause when asking why doesn't yield any more useful information.

4. Continue asking why until the root causes are identified.

5. Always focus on the process aspects of a problem rather than the personalities involved. Finding scapegoats does not solve problems!

Five Whys of Less Vigorous Exercise	
1. Too much TV and video games	*Why?*
2. Few community-sponsored recreation activities	*Why?*
3. No family recreational activities	*Why?*
4. No safe play area	*Why?*
5. Lack of resources	*Why?*

Figure 11 Five Whys example of less vigorous exercise.[6]

MORE:

- Case study – New Breed Logistics: http://rube.asq. org/2009/02/lean/improving-productivity-lean-six- sigma-warehouse-design.pdf

- SQBOK example: http://asq.org/service/ body-of-knowledge/tools-5whys

FLOWCHART

A flowchart is a graphic representation of the flow of a process. It is useful for the following:

- To examine how the various steps in a process relate to each other

- To define the boundaries of the process

- To verify and identify customer-supplier relationships in a process

- To create common understanding of the process flow

- To determine the current "best method" of performing the process

- To identify redundancy and unnecessary complexity

A flowchart provides the visualization of a process by the use of symbols that represent different types of actions, activities, or situations. The rounded-rectangle symbol indicates the beginning or end of the process. Boxes indicate action items and diamonds indicate decision points. Figure 12 displays a process flowchart for getting a cup of coffee. The symbols used are connected with arrows that show the flow of information between the symbols used to represent the steps in the process.

The basic steps involved in creating a flowchart are:

1. Select the process to chart.

2. Determine whether to develop a high-level or detailed flowchart.

3. Define the boundaries of the selected process.

4. Identify the "start block" and place it on the top left corner of the page.

5. Identify the "finish block," or the end point, and place it on the bottom right corner of the page.

6. Try to identify the easiest and most efficient way to go from the "start block" to the "finish block." Though this step isn't absolutely necessary, it does make it easier to do the next step.

7. Document each step in sequence, starting with the first (or last) step.

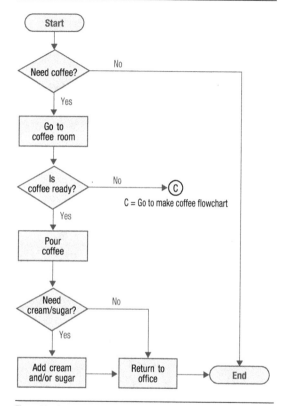

Figure 12 Flowchart example for getting a cup of coffee.

8. Use the appropriate symbol for each step (see Figure 13).

9. Be sure to chart how the work is actually done, not how it is supposed to be done.

10. At each decision point, choose one branch and continue flowcharting that section of the process.

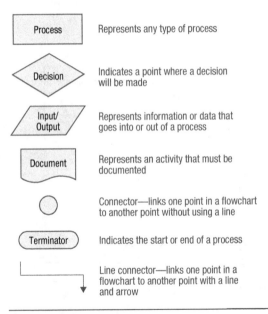

Figure 13 Basic flowchart symbols.

11. If a segment of the process is unfamiliar to everyone, make a note and continue flowcharting.

12. Repeat steps 6, 7, and 8 until that section of the process is complete. Go back and flowchart the other branches from the decision symbols.

13. Identify all the areas that hinder your process or add little or no value.

14. After the flowchart is accurate and complete, analyze it.

Note: You can put the steps of your process on index cards or sticky-back notes. This lets you rearrange the diagram without erasing and redrawing, and prevents ideas from being discarded simply because it's too much work to redraw the diagram.

A completed flowchart:

- Shows how the process actually occurs

- Encourages communication between customers and suppliers

- Illustrates the relationship of various steps in a process

- Educates team members about all the steps within the process

- Can be used to train new employees involved in the process

- Helps set the boundaries of the process

- Identifies team members needed

- Shows where the process can be improved

- Is useful for data collection

- May identify immediate improvement opportunities

Failure to document the actual process is an important pitfall that should be avoided. This can occur when the process is drawn as it was designed and not as it actually happens, or when team members are reluctant to draw parts of the process that might expose weaknesses in their areas. It could also be the case that rework loops are seen as small and unimportant (they aren't!) and are excluded. In extreme cases, it might simply be that team members truly do not know how the process operates.

MORE:

- Case study – JDSU: http://rube.asq.org/2009/09/lean/getting-green-with-lean.pdf

- Case study – Vancouver Coastal Health: http://rube.asq.org/2012/11/lean/emergency-department-congestion.pdf

- Article – "Perfect Match": http://rube.asq.org/six-sigma/2009/08/process-management/perfect-match.pdf

- SQBOK example: http://asq.org/service/body-of-knowledge/tools-flow-chart

FORCE-FIELD ANALYSIS

Force-field analysis (FFA) is a tool that uses a creative process for encouraging agreement about all facets of a desired change. It is used for clarifying and strengthening the "driving forces" for change. For example, what things are "driving" us toward school improvement?

It can also be used to identify obstacles to change, or "restraining forces." Continuing the school example, what is "restraining" us from achieving increased test scores?

Finally, it can be used to encourage agreement on the relative priority of factors on each side of the balance sheet.

To create an FFA diagram, start by drawing a large letter T on a piece of paper. Write the issue at the top of the paper. As a group, describe the ideal situation, and write the resolution in the upper right-hand corner of the paper. See Figure 14 for an FFA diagram related to school improvement.

Have a facilitator work with the group to brainstorm forces leading to or preventing the ideal situation. These forces may be internal or external. List positive forces on the left side of the T and forces restraining movement on the right side. Users of FFA often vary the length of the horizontal arrow lines to indicate the relative strength of each of the forces.

Once all positive and negative forces are listed, prioritize the forces to be strengthened or identify the restraining forces to be minimized in order to accomplish the goal. For example, in this instance the facilitator would keep discussion going among the participants until consensus is reached on each impediment to increasing student test scores.

Issue: School Improvement

Ideal state: An effective learning environment

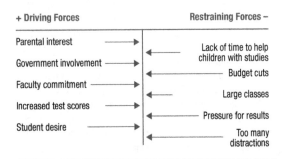

Figure 14   Force-field analysis diagram example.

Force-field analysis encourages team members to raise questions and concerns throughout the process. These concerns and questions shouldn't be considered obstacles to be rejected, but should instead be valued. The process of openly addressing differences of opinion encourages diversity in the planning process.

Force-field analysis is a powerful tool that encourages communication at all levels of management. By creating a structured environment for problem solving, it minimizes feelings of defensiveness. There is a feeling of openness about problem solving because all members of the group are focused on the issue rather than on personal agendas. FFA inhibits hierarchical or traditional power structures that are likely to restrict the flow of creative ideas.

MORE:

- Online example: http://asq.org/healthcare-use/
  why-quality/force-field.html

- SQBOK example: http://asq.org/service/
  body-of-knowledge/tools-force-field

HISTOGRAM

A histogram is a bar chart used to plot the frequency with which different values of a given variable occur. Histograms are used to examine existing patterns, identify the range of variables, and suggest a central tendency in variables.

An example would be to line up, by height, a group of people in a class. Normally, one would be the tallest, one would be the shortest, and there would be a cluster of people around an average height; hence the phrase "normal distribution." This tool helps identify the cause of problems in a process by the shape as well as the width of the distribution.

The histogram evolved to meet the need to evaluate data that occurs at a certain frequency. This is possible because it allows for a concise portrayal of information in a bar graph format. This tool clearly portrays information on location, spread, and shape. It can also help suggest both the nature of and possible improvements for the mechanisms at work in the process. When combined with the concept of the normal curve and knowledge of a particular process, the histogram becomes an effective, practical working tool for use in the early stages of data analysis.

A histogram may be interpreted by asking three questions:

1. Is the process performing within specification limits?

2. Does the process seem to exhibit wide variation?

3. If action needs to be taken on the process, what action is appropriate?

The answers to these three questions lie in analyzing three characteristics of the histogram:

1. How well is the histogram centered? The centering of the data provides information on the process aim above or below some mean or nominal value.

2. How wide is the histogram? Histogram width defines the variability of the process above or below the target value.

3. What is the shape of the histogram? Remember that the data are expected to form a normal or bell-shaped curve. Any significant change or anomaly usually indicates that there is something going on in the process causing the quality problem.

Figure 15 shows a histogram with an abnormal distribution. In this illustration, there is not a normal bell curve of distribution. Rather, there is a drop in frequency of one-pound bags containing 16.75 ounces of flour. It appears that the filling process more frequently fills the bags with more than 16.0 ounces of flour, but not in a normal distribution across ounce values between 16.15 and 17.05.

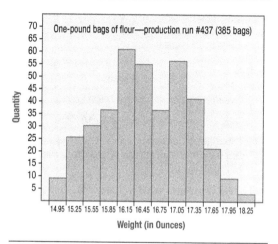

Figure 15 Histogram example.

The basic steps involved in developing a histogram are:

1. Determine the type of data you want to collect.

2. Be sure that the data are measurable (for example, time, length, and speed).

3. Collect as many measurable data points as possible.

4. Collect data on one parameter at a time.

5. Count the total number of points you have collected.

6. Determine the number of intervals required.

7. Determine the range. To do this, subtract the smallest value in the dataset from the largest. This value is the range of your dataset.

8. Determine the interval width. To do this, divide the range by the number of intervals.

9. Determine the starting point of each interval.

10. Draw horizontal (x) and vertical (y) axis lines.

11. Label the horizontal axis to indicate what is being displayed and mark the unit of measure (smallest to largest values).

12. Label the vertical axis to indicate what is being measured and mark the unit of measure (smallest to largest values).

13. Plot the data. Construct vertical bars for each of the values, with the height corresponding to the frequency of occurrence of each value.

MORE:

- Case study – Akron Children's Hospital: http://rube.asq.org/2011/04/six-sigma/reducing-wait-for-mri-exams-gives-akron-childrens-hospital-competitive-edge.pdf

- Case study – U.S. Navy Ship Maintenance Facility, Japan: http://rube.asq.org/2009/11/lean/kaizen-to-shorten-long-turnaround.pdf

- Webcast – "An Introduction to the Seven Basic Quality Tools": http://asq.org/2011/08/quality-tools/an-introduction-to-the-seven-basic-quality-tools-webcast.html

MULTIVOTING

Multivoting is a quick and easy way for a group to identify the items of the highest priority in a list. This technique helps a team to prioritize items on a large list without creating a win-lose situation in the group that generated the list. It also helps separate the "vital few" items from the "useful many" on a large list.

The basic steps involved in multivoting are:

1. Give each team member a number of votes equal to approximately half the number of items on the list (for example, 10 votes for a 20-item list).

2. Have the members vote individually for the items they believe have high priority. Voters can "spend" their votes as they wish, even giving all to one item.

3. Compile the votes given to each item and record the quantity of votes beside each item.

4. Select the four to six items receiving the highest number of votes.

5. Discuss and prioritize the selected items relative to each other. If there is difficulty in reaching agreement, remove the items that received the fewest votes from the list and then conduct another vote.

Multivoting is best suited for use with large groups and long lists. Its simplicity makes it very quick and easy to do.

MORE:

- SQBOK example: http://asq.org/service/body-of-knowledge/tools-multivoting

NOMINAL GROUP TECHNIQUE

Nominal group technique (NGT) is a structured process that identifies and ranks major problems or issues to be addressed. It can be used to identify the major strengths of a department/unit/institution or to make decisions by consensus when selecting problem solutions in a business. This technique provides each participant with an equal voice.

The basic steps involved in using NGT are:

1. Request that all participants (usually 5 to 10 persons) write or say which problem or issue they feel is most important.

2. Record all the problems or issues.

3. Develop a master list of the problems or issues.

4. Generate and distribute to each participant a form that numbers the problems or issues in no particular order.

5. Request that each participant rank the top five problems or issues by assigning five points to their most important perceived problem and one point to the least important of their top five.

6. Tally the results by adding the points for each problem or issue.

7. The problem or issue with the highest number is the most important one for the team as a whole.

8. Discuss the results and generate a final ranked list for process improvement action planning.

MORE:

- Case study – Cedar Rapids Community School District: http://rube.asq.org/2007/05/baldrige-national-quality-program/iowa-school-district-charts-path-for-continuous-improvement.pdf

PARETO CHART

A Pareto chart is a graphic representation of the frequency with which certain events occur. Pareto charts are bar charts, prioritized in descending order from left to right, used to identify the vital few opportunities for improvement. It shows where to put your initial effort to get the most gain.

Figure 16 is an example of a Pareto chart. The chart appears much the same as a histogram or bar chart. The bars are arranged in decreasing order of magnitude from left to right along the x-axis, excepting an "other" category.

The Pareto chart was derived from the 19th century Italian sociologist and economist Vilfredo Pareto's 80/20 rule. Pareto noticed that 80% of the wealth in Italy was held by 20% of the people. Later, Juran noticed that this rule could also be applied to the causes of defects: 80% of defects are due to only 20% of causes. Therefore, by minimizing 20% of the causes, we can eliminate 80% of the problems.

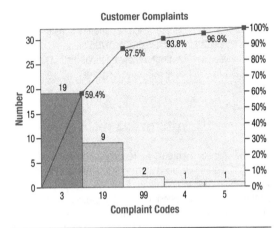

Figure 16 Pareto chart example.

The basic steps involved in constructing a Pareto chart are as follows:

1. Define the measurement scale for the potential causes. (This is usually the frequency of occurrence or cost.)

2. Define the time period during which to collect data about the potential causes (days, weeks, or as much time as is required to observe a significant number of occurrences).

3. Collect and tally data for each potential cause.

4. Label the horizontal (x) axis with all the possible root causes in descending order of value.

5. Label the measurement scale on the vertical (y) axis.

6. Draw one bar for each possible cause to represent the value of the measurement.

7. If desired, add a vertical (y) axis on the right side of the chart to represent cumulative percentage values.

8. Draw a line to show the cumulative percentage from left to right as each cause is added to the chart.

MORE:

- Case study – CRC: http://rube.asq.org/2006/04/cost-of-quality/using-cost-of-quality-to-improve-business-results.pdf

- Case study – Red Cross Hospital, the Netherlands: http://rube.asq.org/quality-engineering/2009/01/lean/quality-quandaries-health-carequalityreducing-the-lengthof-stay-at-a-hospital.pdf

- SQBOK example: http://asq.org/service/body-of-knowledge/tools-pareto-chart

- Webcast – "An Introduction to the Seven Basic Quality Tools": http://asq.org/2011/08/quality-tools/an-introduction-to-the-seven-basic-quality-tools-webcast.html

PICK MATRIX

This Lean-Six Sigma tool was developed by Lockheed Martin to aid in decision making and prioritization of important topics and/or projects. It's a way to visually rank them from the least attractive to the most attractive. The acronym PICK is derived from the four designations given to potential topics or projects being considered:

- Possible – Low impact, easy to do.

- Implement – High impact, easy to do.

- Challenge – High impact, hard to do. In many cases, it's then useful to break these down into smaller components.

- Kill – Low impact, hard to do.

Figure 17 shows a PICK matrix. In the matrix, topics or projects are plotted with dots/x's where they are believed to fall in terms of payoff and difficulty. When the PICK matrix is completed, it is easy to see at a glance which issue(s) to tackle immediately and which will require more time and/or resources to accomplish.

MORE:

- Case study – New Breed Logistics: http://asq. org/2009/02/lean/improving-productivity-lean-six-sigma-warehouse-design.pdf

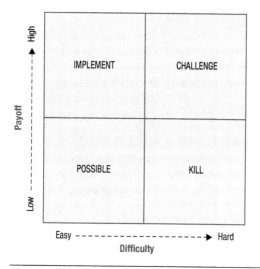

Figure 17　PICK matrix.

RELATIONS DIAGRAM (INTERRELATIONSHIP DIGRAPH)

The relations diagramming method is a technique developed to clarify intertwined causal relationships in a complex situation in order to find an appropriate solution.

Relations diagrams might be used to:

- Determine and develop quality assurance policies
- Establish promotional plans for total quality control introduction
- Design steps to counter market complaints
- Improve quality in the manufacturing process (especially in planning to eliminate latent defects)
- Promote quality control in purchased or ordered items
- Provide measures against troubles related to payment and process control
- Promote small group activities effectively
- Reform administrative and business departments

The digraph in Figure 18 shows some of the interrelating factors pertaining to ongoing and proposed projects within a local school.

MORE:

- Case study – Winston Campus Elementary: http://rube.asq.org/2009/09/continuous-improvement/pdsa-road-map-writing-skills.pdf

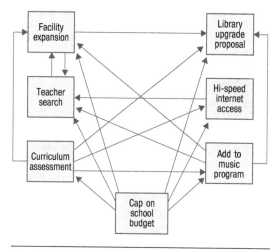

Figure 18   Relations diagram (interrelationship digraph) example.

RUN CHART

A run chart is a line graph that shows data points plotted in the order in which they occur. This type of chart is used to reveal trends and shifts in a process over time, to show variation over time, or to identify decline or improvement in a process over time. It can be used to examine both variables and attribute data.

The data must be collected in a chronological or sequential form starting from and ending at any point. For best results, 25 or more samples must be taken in order to get an accurate run chart.

The chart in Figure 19 plots the average rod diameter of each of 10 lots of rods. A lot is one day's total run.

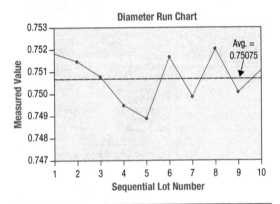

Figure 19 Run chart example.

A run chart shows the history and pattern of variation. It is helpful to indicate on the chart whether up is good or down is good.

The basic steps involved in constructing a run chart are:

1. Construct a horizontal (x) axis line and a vertical (y) axis line.

2. Use the horizontal axis to represent time.

3. Use the vertical axis to represent the values of measurement or the frequency at which an event occurs.

4. Collect data for an appropriate number of time periods, in accordance with your data collection strategy.

5. Plot a point for each time a measurement is taken.

6. Connect the points with a line.

7. Identify questions that the data should answer about the process. Record any questions or observations that can be made as a result of the data.

8. Compute the average for subsequent blocks of time, or after a significant change has occurred.

Keeping in mind the process, interpret the chart. If the process has changed enough to no longer be in control, possible signals are:

- Six points in a row that steadily increase or decrease

- Nine points in a row that are on the same side of the average

- Other patterns such as significant shifts in levels, cyclical patterns, and bunching of data points

Run charts provide information that helps to:

- Identify trends in which more points are above or below the average. When a larger number of points lie either above or below the average, this indicates that there has been an unusual event and that the average has changed. Such changes should be investigated.

- Identify trends in which several points steadily
  increase or decrease with no reversals. Neither
  pattern would be expected based on random chance.
  This would likely indicate an important change and
  the need to investigate.

- Identify common and special cause variation within
  a process.

MORE:

- Case study – Hunting Ridge School, Palatine, IL:
  http://rube.asq.org/2009/08/quality-tools/quality-
  club-tomorrows-leaders.pdf

- SQBOK example: http://asq.org/service/
  body-of-knowledge/tools-run-chart

SCATTER DIAGRAM

A scatter diagram is a chart in which one variable is plotted
against another to determine whether there is a correlation
between the two variables. These diagrams are used to plot
the distribution of information in two dimensions.

Figure 20 shows a plot of two variables—in this example,
predicted values versus observed values. As the predicted
value increases, so does the actual measured value. These
variables are said to be positively correlated; that is, if one
increases, so does the other. The line plotted is a "regression"
line, which shows the average linear relationship between
the variables. If the line in a scatter diagram has a negative
slope, the variables are negatively correlated; that is, when
one increases, the other decreases, and vice versa. When

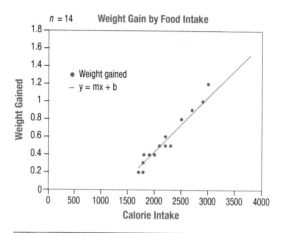

Figure 20 Scatter diagram example.

no regression line can be plotted and the scatter diagram appears to simply be a ball of diffuse points, then the variables are said to be uncorrelated.

The specific utility of finding correlations is to pursue causal relationships among variables and ultimately to find the root causes of problems.

The basic steps involved in constructing a scatter diagram are:

1. Define the x variable on a graph paper scatter diagram form. This variable is often thought of as the cause variable and is typically plotted on the horizontal axis.

2. Define the y variable on the diagram. This variable is often thought of as the effect variable and is typically plotted on the vertical axis.

3. Number the pairs of x and y variable measurements consecutively. Record each pair of measures for x and y in the appropriate columns. Make sure that the x measures and the corresponding y measures remain paired so that the data are accurate.

4. Plot the x and y data pairs on the diagram. Locate the x value on the horizontal axis, and then locate the y value on the vertical axis. Place a point on the graph where these two intersect.

5. Study the shape that is formed by the series of data points plotted. In general, conclusions can be made about the association between two variables (referred to as x and y) based on the shape of the scatter diagram. Scatter diagrams that display associations between two variables tend to look like elliptical spheres or even straight lines.

6. Scatter diagrams on which the plotted points appear in a circular fashion show little or no correlation between x and y.

7. Scatter diagrams on which the points form a pattern of increasing values for both variables show a positive correlation; as values of x increase, so do values of y. The more tightly the points are clustered in a linear fashion, the stronger the positive correlation, or the association between the two variables.

8. Scatter diagrams on which one variable increases in value while the second variable decreases in value

show a negative correlation between x and y. Again,
the more tightly the points are clustered in a linear
fashion, the stronger the association between the two
variables.

It's crucial to remember that scatter diagrams show only
that a relationship exists between two variables, not that one
variable causes the other. Further analysis using advanced
statistical techniques can quantify how strong the relationship
is between two variables.

MORE:

- Article – "Fair or Foul?: The innovative Moneyball
  management approach can make a difference—up
  to a point": http://asq.org/quality-progress/2012/04/
  strategic-planning/fair-or-foul.html

- Article – "Quality Quandaries: Process Regime
  Changes": http://rube.asq.org/pub/qe/2007/
  vol19-no1/quality-quandaries-process-regime-
  changes.pdf

- Article – "Building From the Basics: Master these
  quality tools and do your job better": http://asq.org/
  quality-progress/2009/01/basic-quality/building-from-
  the-basics.html

- SQBOK example: http://asq.org/service/
  body-of-knowledge/tools-scatter-plot

- Webcast – "An Introduction to the Seven Basic
  Quality Tools": http://asq.org/2011/08/quality-tools/
  an-introduction-to-the-seven-basic-quality-tools-
  webcast.html

TREE DIAGRAM

A tree diagram is a graphic representation of the separation of broad, general information into increasing levels of detail. The tool ensures that action plans remain visibly linked to overall goals, that actions flow logically from identified goals, and that the true level of a project's complexity will be fully understood. The goal to establish objectives for improving operations is diagrammed in Figure 21.

Tree diagrams are used in the quality planning process. The diagram begins with a generalized goal (the tree trunk) and then identifies progressively finer levels of actions (the branches) needed to accomplish the goal. As part of process improvement, it can be used to help identify root causes of trouble. The tool is especially useful in designing new products or services and in creating an implementation plan to remedy identified process problems. In order for the diagram to accurately reflect the project, it is essential that the team using it have a detailed understanding of the tasks required.

The steps involved in generating a tree diagram are:

1. Identify the goal statement or primary objective. This should be a clear, action-oriented statement to which the entire team agrees. Such statements may come from the root cause/driver identified in an interrelationship digraph or from the headings of an affinity diagram. Write this goal on the extreme left of the chart.

2. Subdivide the goal statement into major secondary categories. These branches should represent goals, activities, or events that lead to the primary objective

or that are required to achieve the overall goal. The
team should continually ask, "What is required to
meet this condition?" "What happens next?" and
"What needs to be addressed?" Write the secondary
categories to the right of the goal statement. Using
sticky-back notes at this stage makes later changes
easier to accomplish.

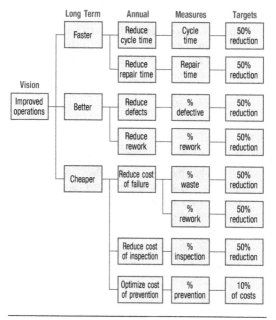

Figure 21   Tree diagram example.

3. Break each major heading into greater detail. As you move from left to right in the tree, the tasks and activities should become more and more specific. Stop the breakdown of each level once there are assignable tasks. If the team does not have enough knowledge to continue at some point, identify the individuals who can supply the information and continue the breakdown later with those individuals present.

4. Review the diagram for logic and completeness. Make sure that each subheading and path has a direct cause-and-effect relationship with the one before. Examine the paths to ensure that no obvious steps have been left out. Also ensure that the completion of listed actions will indeed lead to the anticipated results.

MORE:

- Case study – U.S. Naval Ship Repair Facility, Japan: http://rube.asq.org/2007/04/ environmental-management-and-sustainability/ reworking-equipment-and-methods-speeds- environmental-cleanup.pdf

- Case study – Singapore Housing and Development Board: http://rube.asq.org/2009/06/quality-tools/ magic-huddles.pdf

- Webcast – "The Seven Management and Planning Tools Webcast Series Overview": http://asq. org/2010/06/quality-tools/the-seven-management- and-planning-tools-webcast-series-overview.html

Part III
Customer–Supplier Relationships

Whatever your role and whatever industry your organization is part of, you have customers and suppliers. You are both a customer *and* supplier, in some manner. If that's unclear, it will be explained below.

Customer–supplier relationships exist in all shapes and forms, and they are crucial to your business. They're even *more* crucial if you want to implement quality practices. Analyzing the feedback from customers and suppliers is one way to know that what you're doing is meeting expectations. How can you improve what you're doing? By analyzing the feedback and by maintaining a healthy relationship with your vendors and suppliers. They can help by doing things like giving you better materials, not damaging things you hand off to them before they go to customers, and so on.

Throughout the following discussion, we occasionally use the word "product" alone. In all cases, we are also referring to services. This information applies equally to product-based and service-based organizations.

CUSTOMERS

Internal

Internal customers are those within the organization. Every function and workgroup in an organization is both a receiver of services and/or products or services from internal and/or external sources and a provider of services and/or products to internal and/or external customers. These interfaces between provider and receiver may be one to one, one to many, many to one, or many to many. Each receiver has needs and requirements. Whether or not the delivered service or product meets the needs and requirements of the receiver, it impacts the effectiveness and quality of services and/or products to their customers, and so on.

The steps to improve processes and services are as follows:

1. Identify internal customer interfaces (providers of services/products and receivers of their services/products).

2. Establish internal customer service/product needs and requirements.

3. Ensure that internal customer requirements are consistent with and supportive of external customer requirements.

4. Document service-level agreements between providers and receivers.[7]

5. Establish improvement goals and measurements.

6. Implement systems for tracking and reporting performance and for supporting the continuous improvement of the process.

Effect of Treatment of Internal Customers on That of External Customers

Careless behavior of management (and management systems) toward internal customers may in turn create careless or indifferent treatment of external customers. Be wary if you see any of the following in your organization:

- Poor tools and equipment

- Defective or late material from a previous operation

- Incorrect/incomplete instructions

- Illegible work orders or prints

- Circumvention of worker safety procedures and practices

- Unhealthy work environment

- Lack of interest in internal complaints

- Disregard for external customer feedback

These can generate a downward spiral that could adversely affect an organization's business. Ignoring the needs of internal customers makes it very difficult to instill a desire to care for the needs of external customers. The surly and uncooperative salesperson, waitperson, housekeeping employee, healthcare provider, delivery person, or customer service representative is often a reflection of an organization's lack of caring for its internal customers.

External

External customers are those who are served by or who receive products or services from the supplier organization. There are many types of external customers:

1. Consumers/end users
   - *Retail buyer of products/services.* The retail buyer influences the design and usability of product features and accessories based on the volume purchased. Consumer watchdog organizations warn purchasers of potential problems. The factors important to this type of buyer, depending on the type of product or service, are: reasonable price, ease of use, performance, safety, aesthetics, durability, ease of purchase process, installation, instructions for use, post-purchase service, warranty period, packaging, friendliness of seller's personnel, and brand name. Increasingly, retail buyers also consider the organization's social responsibility standing: reputation, ethics, environmental practices, human rights record, and so on.
   - *Discount buyer.* The discount buyer shops primarily for price, is more willing to accept less-well-known brands, and is willing to buy quantities in excess of immediate needs. These buyers have relatively little influence on the products, except for, perhaps, creating a market for off-brands, production surpluses, and discontinued items.
   - *Employee buyer.* The employee buyer purchases the employer's products, usually at a deep

discount. Such procurement activities can be a part of a person's role for their employer. Often being familiar with or even a contributor to the products bought, this buyer can provide valuable feedback to the employer both directly, through surveys, and indirectly, through volume and items purchased.

- *Service buyer.* The buyer of services (such as TV repair, dental work, and tax preparation) often buys inspired by word-of-mouth, either literal or online. Word of good or poor service spreads rapidly and influences the continuance of the service provider's business.

- *Service user.* The captive service user (such as the user of electricity, gas, water, municipal services, and schools) generally has little choice regarding from which supplier they receive services. Until competition is introduced, there is little incentive for providers to vary their services.

- *Organization buyer.* Buyers for organizations that use a product or service in the course of business or activity can have a significant influence on the types of products offered as well as on the organization from which they buy. Raw materials or devices that become part of a manufactured product are especially critical in sustaining quality and competitiveness for the buyer's organization (including performance, serviceability, price, ease of use, durability, simplicity of design, safety, and ease of disposal). Other factors include: flexibility in delivery, discounts, allowances for returned material, extraordinary guarantees, and so on.

Factors that particularly pertain to purchased services are the reputation and credibility of the provider, range of services offered, degree of customization offered, timeliness, fee structure, etc.

2. Intermediate customers

- *Wholesale buyer.* Wholesalers buy what they expect they can sell. They typically buy in large quantities. They may have little direct influence on product design and manufacture, but they do influence the providers' production schedules, pricing policies, warehousing and delivery arrangements, return policies for unsold merchandise, and so on.

- *Distributor.* Distributors are similar to wholesalers in some ways but differ in that they may stock a wider variety of products from a wide range of producers. What they stock is directly influenced by their customers' demands and needs. Their customers' orders are often small and may consist of a mix of products. The distributors' forte is stocking thousands of catalog items that can be "picked" and shipped on short notice at an attractive price. Customers seeking quality at a good price and immediately available mainly influence distributors stocking commodity-type items such as sheet metal, construction materials, mineral products, and stationary items. "Blanket orders" for a yearly quantity delivered at specified intervals are prevalent for some materials.

- *Retail chain buyer.* Buyers for large retail chains, because of the size of their orders, place major demands on their providers. These demands include pricing concessions, flexible deliveries, assumption of warehousing costs for already-purchased products, special packaging requirements, no-cost return policy, and electronic order processing.

- *Other volume buyers.* Government entities, educational institutions, healthcare organizations, transportation companies, public utilities, cruise lines, hotel chains, and restaurant chains all represent large-volume buyers that provide services to customers. Such organizations have regulations governing their services. Each requires a wide range of products, materials, and external services, most of which are transparent to the consumer. Each requires high quality and each has tight limitations on what it can pay (based on appropriations, cost-control mandates, tariffs, or heavy competition). Each such buyer demands much for its money but may offer long-term contracts for fixed quantities. The buying organizations' internal customers frequently influence the products required.

- *Service providers.* The diversity of service providers buying products and services from other providers is mind-boggling. These buyers include plumbers, public accountants, dentists, doctors, building contractors, cleaning services, computer programmers, web site designers, consultants, manufacturer's reps, actors, and taxi

drivers, among many others. This type of buyer,
often self-employed, buys very small quantities,
shops for value, buys only when the product or
service is needed (when the buyer has a job,
patient, or client), and relies on high quality of
purchases to maintain customers' satisfaction.
This buyer is influenced by a provider's ability to
furnish service and/or replacement parts for old
or obsolete equipment, ability to supply extremely
small quantities of an extremely large number of
products (such as those supplied by a hardware
store, construction materials depot, or medical
products supply house), and product knowledge
that extends to knowing how the product is to
be used.

With some exceptions (such as very small organizations),
most organizations segment their customer base in order
to better serve the needs of different types of customers.
Customers may be segmented by:

- Purchase volume
- Profitability (to the selling organization)
- Industry classification
- Geographic factors (such as municipalities, regions, states, countries, and continents)
- Demographic factors (such as age, income, marital status, education, and gender)
- Psychographic factors (such as values, beliefs, and attitudes)

Providing the exact same product or service to every type of customer is no longer feasible. Henry Ford is reported to have said, "People can have the Model T in any color— so long as it's black." Black was the only paint color available that dried fast enough to allow Ford's assembly-line approach to work. Does this attitude still seem valid in any industry today?

An organization must decide whether it is interested in simply pursuing more customers (or contributors, in the case of a not-for-profit fund-raiser) or in targeting the right customers. It is not unusual for an organization, after segmenting its customer base, to find that it is not economically feasible to continue to serve a particular segment. Conversely, an organization may find that it is uniquely capable of further penetrating a particular market segment, or may even discover a niche not presently served by other organizations.

CUSTOMER FEEDBACK

Customer relationship management (CRM), also referred to as relationship marketing or one-to-one marketing (serving the unique needs of each customer), is receiving emphasis in today's fast-paced, ever-changing environment. CRM relates less to the product or service provided and more to the way business is conducted. In a customer-focused organization, the thrust is usually more toward nurturing existing customers than a drive to attract new customers. A key principle of good customer relations is determining and ensuring customer satisfaction.

Perceptions of customer satisfaction must be corroborated or rejected through sound means for collecting, analyzing, and acting upon customer feedback. Effective systems for utilizing customer feedback involve several elements:

- Formal processes exist for collecting, measuring, and analyzing customer data and for communicating results to the appropriate business functions for action.

- Feedback mechanisms are in place to determine how well an organization is meeting customer requirements.

- Most organizations choose a combination of methods to get a more complete picture. Once customer satisfaction data have been gathered, sophisticated techniques can be used to analyze the data and target areas for improvement.

- Data are stored appropriately and made available to those who need it.

Some examples of the origins of customer data that can be useful in determining customer needs and satisfaction are:

Data from within the organization

- Customer complaints, when logged and tracked

- Past records of claim resolutions

- Product warranty registration cards and guarantee usage

- Service records—product failure, product maintenance

- Input from customer contact personnel
- Customer satisfaction surveys
- Transaction data
- Data from established "listening posts"
- Lost-customer analysis
- Market research

Data from outside the organization

- Data about competitors' customers
- Research including magazine and newspaper articles, trade journal information
- Public information including customers' and competitors' annual reports
- Advertising media including brochures, TV, radio, websites
- Industry market research

Table 2 presents different levels of customer satisfaction.

Level	Is Your Customer:	Then Your Customer:
1	dissatisfied?	has probably departed forever.
2	marginally satisfied?	is casual (any supplier will do).
3	basically satisfied?	is borderline, uncommitted.
4	delighted?	is a return customer (retained).
5	a committed advocate?	is loyal, appreciates what you do, and tells others.

Table 2   Levels of customer satisfaction.

We'll now discuss a few of these customer feedback concepts in greater detail.

Complaints

Complaint data, when appropriately captured and analyzed provides a wealth of information about customer satisfaction. However, it must be realized that the data do not constitute a valid statistical sample: Many customers find it a burden to complain unless there is a serious problem, and the majority of customers have no discernible complaint to register.

Many organizations openly solicit complaints. Think of the restaurant waitperson who inquires about your satisfaction with your food; the organization that serves mail-order customers and includes a self-addressed, stamped reply card; the hotel that seeks feedback on your satisfaction with your stay at its facility; or the online store that emails you a link to a survey about your shopping and purchasing experience on their website. Buyer satisfaction is greatly improved when a complaint is quickly resolved, as is a customer's intent to repurchase from a supplier.

Customer Surveys

Many organizations solicit customer feedback with formal customer surveys. The aims of a survey are to get as high a response rate as possible, to obtain the most representative sampling of the customer population surveyed, and to acquire as much useful data as possible. Designing surveys and analyzing the data received are processes involving much expertise and knowledge. Administering the survey process is expensive. Misinterpretation and inappropriate use of the data can be even more expensive.

Methods of administering surveys include:

- Mail
- Electronic (e-mail or through a website)
- Telephone
- In person, one-to-one
- In person, group
- In person, panel

Each method has its advantages and disadvantages. The relative effectiveness of one over another also depends on the purpose of the survey, the population to be surveyed, and the benefit-to-cost ratio of conducting the survey. For example, one-to-one interviews can generally only reach a small number of persons and are expensive to conduct, but the personal contact involved often yields great insights. The mailed survey has its costs but can reach unlimited numbers of potential respondents. The response rate can be low and the types of customers responding may not represent a reasonable sample. This method, however, is far less expensive than one-to-one surveys. Electronic surveys are relatively inexpensive when integrated with other website material, but they can yield very low response rates and may produce responses from only the wildly delighted, the highly dissatisfied customers, and the "loyal" customers willing to help.

The organization should word questions at a level that the customer can understand, and not formulate questions' content based solely on what it thinks the customer would want to answer.

It's important to select a random and representative group of customers. Not doing so will result in responses that are not statistically valid. This can also happen when a low quantity of responses is analyzed. Any analysis done from such a sampling won't be valid since the extremes of satisfaction and dissatisfaction tend to respond to surveys more frequently than those who are neutral.

Analyze survey results closely. Taking action based on answers to inept or misdirected questions can cause the organization to focus on the wrong or less important improvement effort. Then use sound survey results analysis in the organization's strategic planning and continuous improvement efforts.

Transaction Data

Many organizations collect a wealth of data about their customers through direct interaction with them. Examples include data collected on consumer buying habits through the use of store-issued identification cards (the use of the cards is supported by discount incentives) and through the analysis of "hits" and "buys" from users of websites.

Another way to gather transaction data is to engage external "mystery shoppers" to make purchases of your product and provide feedback to your organization about the experience. (The same approach is also used to "shop" the competitors and check out their approaches.)

Data From Established "Listening Posts"

Organizations have many employees who periodically interact with counterparts at customer or supplier organizations:

engineer to engineer, salesperson to salesperson, CEO to CEO, delivery person to receiving person, and so on. In a majority of these interactions, whether face-to-face or via telephone, fax, or e-mail, the customers' people express opinions, suggestions, complaints, or compliments about the supplier's organization, the quality of its products/services, delivery, price—even about the level of personal attention they receive. Excepting severe negative expressions, these comments, casually and informally made, are seldom captured. Be sure to do so! Having a formal process for collecting and analyzing these data allows an organization to spot the early stages of an eventual customer problem. It also permits the direction of compliments to the responsible people as positive feedback.[8]

Tracking, Measuring, and Reporting

Producing tabulations of customer satisfaction data, trend charts, and so forth is of minimal value without an established objective against which to compare. To make sense of the time and energy involved in collecting the data, there must be a target. To justify preventive action that may be indicated by the analyzed data, there must be a basis for estimating the anticipated gain to be achieved by the action, a means for tracking progress toward achieving the objective, and a basis for evaluating the effectiveness of the action taken.

Simplified steps for determining what it is worth to retain customers are:

1. Segment the customer base by types of products or services sold to each segment.

2. Select an appropriate time period (for customers buying consumer products, perhaps 2 years; for homeowner insurance buyers, maybe 30 years).

3. Compute the average annual profit each customer segment produces. For example, the annual value of the home computer buyer segment equals the average initial purchase price (including a three-year service contract) plus the average price of add-ons purchased within the three years, divided by three, times the number of customers in this segment.

4. Compute the value of each retained customer. To the value of an individual customer in this segment, add the dollar value of upgrading the customer to a new computer at the end of the three-year period. Determine how many customer upgrades represent a challenging but possible goal. Multiply the individual customer's figure by this number of upgrades. This is what it is worth to retain your customers through their first upgrade.

5. Determine what actions are needed, based on your customer satisfaction data, to retain your present customers and estimate the cost of these actions.

6. Compute the estimated net gain from customer retention efforts—the worth of customers minus cost to retain the customers.[9]

7. Do this for each segment. Note: Some segments may not be worth added retention effort. You may also discover a segment of customers for which even initial efforts to sell to them may not be economically wise.

Kano Model

In an organization's efforts to increase customer satisfaction, it is critical to understand what satisfies customers, what does not, and what new or improved products and services could excite customers. Japanese professor Noriaki Kano devised a model that describes the interrelationship among three product qualities: those qualities that must be present, those that are "delighters" or "exciters," and those that are "one-dimensional." A "must be" quality is a dissatisfier when absent and is acceptable (and often not consciously noticed) when present. A "delighter" is unexpected and is a satisfier. However, over time, a "delighter" becomes a "must be," as in the case of the remote TV controller. A "one-dimensional" quality affects satisfaction in direct relationship to its presence; for example, as the price of gasoline goes down, satisfaction increases. Customer research is often used to determine dissatisfiers, satisfiers, and potential delighters. Problems do arise when an organization *thinks* it knows what its customers need and want without having done adequate testing within the various market segments it purports to serve. See Figure 22 for Kano's model.

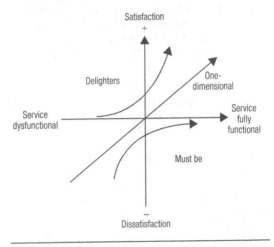

Figure 22 The Kano model.

SUPPLIERS

Internal

Internal suppliers are the "providers" discussed in the earlier section on internal customers. Internal suppliers include not only those providers directly involved in producing the products/services, but also support functions such as tariff checkers in a trucking company, materials management and cost accounting functions in manufacturing, facility maintenance in a school, the pharmacy in a hospital, the motor pool in a government agency, and market research.

In many organizations, internal suppliers establish service-level agreements (SLAs) with their customers. These agreements, usually for primary processes or sub processes, provide the requirements that must be met by the supplier and allow for quantitative measurement of results. Internal data processing and information technology groups have used SLAs for many years to mutually establish customer requirements and measure performance to requirements.

External

Communicating stated expectations and requirements between customer and supplier is frequently a problem. Because of the pressures to acquire and keep business, suppliers often accept poorly communicated requirements.

Often, a smaller organization fears losing business by antagonizing a large and perhaps major customer with more extensive probing as to what the customer really needs. In some situations, this may mean asking the customer more about how and where the supplier's product will be used (usually essential in medical device manufacturing). A commonly used international standard for quality management systems requires the review of contracts and clarification of customer requirements before the acceptance of an order.

Many organizations are changing their approach to external suppliers from the traditional adversarial relationship to a collaborative relationship. In past times, a supplier (more often called a "vendor") was considered an entity beneath the status of the buying organization. The "purchasing agent" of old would seek to pressure vendors until the lowest price was obtained. Often the buying organization was significantly larger than the vendor's organization and wielded the power of offering potentially large orders. Price and delivery were the primary drivers in the vendor selection process. If quality became a problem, an order was canceled and another vendor selected.

Increasingly, buying and selling organizations are forming quasi-partnerships and alliances to collaborate on improving the buyer–seller relationship, as well as the quality of the products or services being purchased. Buying organizations have been able to substantially reduce the number of suppliers for any given product or service and cut costs through improved quality. It is not uncommon now for the buying organization to assist a supplier with training to use quality tools, material handling and stocking practices, and so forth. In this collaboration, the buying organization expects that the established quality and service levels will be consistent with its needs, that the supplier's practices will be continuously improved, and that lower prices will result. The supplier often receives assurance of longer-term contracts, assistance in making improvements, and sometimes certification as a preferred supplier.

SUPPLIER FEEDBACK

Suppliers need to know how they are performing. If suppliers are providing products or services vital to quality, the customer must have a formal process for collecting, analyzing, and reporting supplier performance. Some common assessment and measurement tools for supplier performance are described here.

Questionnaires/Assessments

Suppliers may be asked to complete a survey about how their quality systems are designed and what plans for improvement have been developed. The customer may also conduct on-site assessments.

Survey questionnaires are usually mailed. They may be used to assess prospective or new suppliers or to reassess existing suppliers on a periodic basis. Use of questionnaires is one of the ways suppliers are "qualified" for the customer's qualified supplier list.

The same design comments and cautions that apply to customer surveys pertain here as well. The difference between supplier questionnaires and customer questionnaires is that the customer expects a 100% response from suppliers. Many suppliers begrudgingly fill out the questionnaires because not to do so would mean loss of business. Large customers sometimes require lengthy questionnaires of even their smallest suppliers, without considering the burden placed on the suppliers.

Product Data

Suppliers may be requested to provide product quality data from the pertinent production run with each delivery, which is used in place of formal verification by the customer. The customer may then analyze the data for compliance to specification as well as process stability and capability.

Delivery Performance

Supplier performance against delivery requirements (for example, total number of days early and total days late) is typically tracked and compared against order requirements.

Complaints

Tracking and reporting complaints about supplier performance is necessary in order to maintain a list of qualified suppliers. An unacceptable number of complaints may result in a supplier being suspended from the list, placed on probation, or totally removed. Usually a hierarchy of categories (types of reasons) is devised for use in coding complaints. The acceptance tolerance for numbers of complaints may vary depending upon the category.

Corrective Action

When a problem is reported to a supplier with a formal request for corrective action, a tracking process is needed to ensure that the supplier responds. These records should be analyzed to determine whether the supplier has been timely in its responses as well as effective with its corrective actions. Without good follow-up by the customer, some suppliers will tend to ignore corrective action requests. Making supplier action mandatory through contracts is a way to resolve this situation.

Product Price and Total Cost

Organizations continually try to reduce the cost of raw materials and services, or at least to minimize increases. The ability of suppliers to continually show progress in this arena is encouraged and tracked.

Certification and Rating

Some customers have programs for "certifying" qualified suppliers. Typically, certified suppliers have demonstrated their ability to consistently meet the customer's requirements over a period of time. Suppliers are rated on a predetermined scale that may include most of the measurements already noted, as well as others. As the supplier fulfills the time and rating requirements, the supplier moves up through a two- or three-phase plan to full recognition as a certified supplier. The customer usually provides concessions to the certified supplier, such as no incoming inspection requirement, arrangements to ship directly to stock, a long-term purchasing contract, and "preferred supplier" status.

Rating supplier performance can be done in a number of ways. Boeing, one of the world's largest aerospace companies and the manufacturer of commercial jetliners and defense, space and security systems, uses a color-coded scale for its 17,525 suppliers in 52 countries:

- Red: Unsatisfactory supplier performance, clearly failing to meet expectations

- Yellow: Improvement needed in supplier performance to meet expectations

- Bronze: Satisfactory supplier performance, meeting expectations

- Silver: Very good supplier performance, meeting or exceeding expectations

- Gold: Exceptional supplier performance, clearly exceeding expectations

Boeing calculates these ratings based on the supplier's averaged scores on three criteria: delivery, general performance assessment (GPA), and quality. For more on Boeing's system, see the article "The Way to Engage" in ASQ's *Quality Progress* magazine.[10]

Needless to say, reporting on the supplier's certification, rating, and/or overall performance should be done on a regular basis, such as quarterly.

Driving Continuous Improvement

Material and services from suppliers, when they are direct inputs to the product realization process, can substantially impact product quality, customer satisfaction, and profitability. Efforts to improve incoming material and services from suppliers (including their correctness, completeness, accuracy, timeliness, and appearance) are often given less attention by the customer than the customer's own internal processes. It should be noted, however, that defective material and inadequate services just received have not yet incurred the added costs of the production process. When a product is rejected at any stage up to and including its use by an end user, costs have been added at each stage in the cycle. At any stage, including the failure of a product under warranty, the quality of the incoming material or services could be the real root cause of failure. The tendency of some customers to "work around" supplier deficiencies is not acceptable and will eventually hold the customer back.

Initiatives to continually improve suppliers' performance are critical to building and sustaining customer confidence. As mentioned earlier, the emerging trend of greater collaboration between customers and their suppliers is opening new opportunities for improvement, often developing into partnerships and alliances.

Conclusion

ood news: by learning and using the ideas found in this guide, you will make huge improvements by being more process oriented in your thinking and applying quality tools as needed.

The bad news? You have probably thought it at some point while reading: many problems are extremely difficult to solve and intimidating in scope. A lot of them require advanced thinking and tools described in books that fill entire professional libraries. So what about those problems?

Begin to tackle them by learning more about those "macro" quality models and systems briefly outlined in the section of the same name. Becoming familiar with the concepts and tools in this guide will give you a huge jump-start. In fact, some quality professionals like to say that any new management concept that comes along, from Six Sigma to lean to anything else, is just a repackaged version of the quality basics, and there is some truth to that. In some ways, those models are simply a specific way or sequence to apply a certain portion of the tools.

Despite the impression you might get from a quality fanatic, quality isn't magic. Management simply directing employees to "do quality" or "do Lean-Six Sigma" won't accomplish as much as it could. We won't lie: you *will* see some results even with a partial or half-hearted use of quality management techniques and approaches. They are that powerful. But using the concepts and tools with greater nuance and complexity will, not surprisingly, yield even bigger and better results. With this book at your side, we hope you seek out such results; they will benefit you personally in your career and your organization in its competitiveness and success.

Lastly, we ask you to reflect on the content in this guide. If you were completely new to quality before reading, did we pique your interest? If so, we have provided numerous other resources, many of them completely free, that will allow you to go deeper. Also consider studying for and testing for ASQ's Quality Improvement Associate certification (CQIA). This guide contains much of the content you'll need to know to pass the exam.

Even if we *didn't* interest you in quality, we still want to hear from you. Please email us at authors@asq.org with any feedback you have on how to make this guide more useful to your needs.

Additional Reading

In addition to the following resources, remember that the sections "Quality Models and Systems" and "Tools" also include articles, case studies, books, and webcasts for further study.

The very first book to seek out is *The Quality Improvement Handbook, Second Edition* by the ASQ Quality Management Division and John E. Bauer, Grace L. Duffy, and Russell T. Westcott, editors. Much of the content for this guide was adapted from the *Handbook*. Its content is thus the next step up in depth from this pocket guide.

Auditing

Arter, Dennis R. *Quality Audits for Improved Performance, Third Edition* (Milwaukee: ASQ Quality Press, 2003).

Russell, J.P. *The Internal Auditing Pocket Guide: Preparing, Performing, Reporting and Follow-up, Second Edition* (Milwaukee: ASQ Quality Press, 2007).

Customer-Supplier Relationships

Parks, Kirsten and Timothy Connor. "The Way to Engage" from *Quality Progress* magazine, April 2011 (Milwaukee: ASQ).

Schoenfeldt, Thomas I. *A Practical Application of Supply Chain Management Principles* (Milwaukee: ASQ Quality Press, 2008).

Overview on the ASQ website of supplier quality: http://asq.org/learn-about-quality/supplier-quality/overview/overview.html

Process Management

Andersen, Bjørn, Tom Fagerhaug, Bjørnar Henriksen, and Lars E. Onsøyen. *Mapping Work Processes* (2nd ed.) (Milwaukee: ASQ Quality Press, 2008).

Webcast – "Delivering Process Excellence Through Process Management" by Scott Rutherford, Michael Nichols and Joe Basala: http://asq.org/2012/10/process-management/delivering-process-excellence-through-process-management-webcast-slides.html

Teams

Joiner, Brian L., Barbara J. Streibel, and Peter R. Scholtes. *The Team Handbook* (3rd ed.) (Madison, WI: Oriel Inc., 2003).

Overview on the ASQ website: http://asq.org/learn-about-quality/teams/overview/overview.html

Tools

Andersen, Bjørn. *Business Process Improvement Toolbox* (2nd ed.) (Milwaukee: ASQ Quality Press, 2008).

Tague, Nancy R. *The Quality Toolbox* (2nd ed.) (Milwaukee: ASQ Quality Press, 2005).

Appendix

See Tool Selection Chart on page 134.

Gather ideas	Group ideas	Analyze	Sequence steps	Draw a picture of data	Track data over time	Prioritize or get group consensus	Show relationships
Affinity diagram	Affinity diagram	Cause-and-effect diagram	Flowchart	Histogram	Check sheet	PICK matrix	Relations diagram
Cause-and-effect diagram	Cause-and-effect diagram	Force-field analysis	Arrow diagram	Pareto chart	Run chart	Multivoting	Scatter diagram
Brainstorming		Relations diagram	Tree diagram	Run chart	Pareto chart	Nominal group technique	
Force-field analysis		Pareto chart		Scatter diagram	Control chart	Relations diagram	
Benchmarking		Five whys		Control chart		Decision matrix	
Audit							

Tool selection chart.

Source: Modified from *There Is Another Way!: Launch a Baldrige-Based Quality Classroom, Second Edition,* by Margaret A. Byrnes with Jeanne C. Baxter (ASQ Quality Press, 2013).

End Notes

1. http://www.iso.org/iso/home/news_index/news_archive/news.htm?refid=Ref1665

2. M. L. George. *Lean Six Sigma for Service* (McGraw Hill, New York, 2003):6–9.

3. J.P. Russell. "Game of Chance," *Quality Progress,* August 2012, pp. 52–54.

4. Economou, M. "Quality's not costly." *Manufacturing Engineering* 120, no. 3 (Dearborn, MI: Society of Manufacturing Engineers, 1998): 20.

5. International Organization for Standardization strategic advisory group on corporate social responsibility, preliminary working definition of organizational social responsibility, ISO/TMB AGCSR N4, 2002.

6. Ron Bialek, Grace L. Duffy, John W. Moran. *The Public Health Quality Improvement Handbook* (Quality Press, Milwaukee, WI 2009), p. 170.

7. Westcott, R. T. Quality level agreements for clarity of expectations. *Stepping up to ISO 9004:2000* (Chico, CA: Paton Press, 2003), appendix C.

8. Westcott, R. T. Tapping the customer's many voices. *Stepping up to ISO 9004:2000* (Chico, CA: Paton Press, 2003), appendix B. Article describes the "LCALI" (listen, capture, analyze, learn, and improve) process for establishing listening posts and using the data collected.

9. F. Reicheld, and C. Fornell present a more sophisticated approach to determining the worth of retaining customers in "What's a Loyal Customer Worth?" *Fortune* (December 1995).

10. http://asq.org/quality-progress/2011/04/supplier-quality/the-way-to-engage.html

Index

Note: Page numbers in *italics* indicate figures or tables.

NOTES

NOTES

CPSIA information can be obtained
at www.ICGtesting.com
Printed in the USA
JSHW011412160723
44694JS00004B/14